Y0-BEA-740

SOLAR HEATING: A CONSTRUCTION MANUAL

SOLAR HEATING

A CONSTRUCTION MANUAL

PETER L. TEMPLE

JENNIFER A. ADAMS

TOTAL ENVIRONMENTAL ACTION, INC.
HARRISVILLE, NEW HAMPSHIRE

CHILTON BOOK COMPANY, RADNOR, PENNSYLVANIA

CAUTION: If the directions in this manual are not followed, not only will the system perform poorly, but a dangerous situation could result. For example, if the instructions for power venting the roof collector are not carried out, the resulting high temperatures will seriously degrade nearby wood and may result in a fire. Further, all procedures should be carried out using the recommended materials and the proper tools, as indicated in the manual. Standard and accepted safety precautions should be followed at all times. No design should be modified unless the individual is fully qualified to foresee all the ramifications and possible hazards of such modifications.

Following the index is an 8-page section which constitutes an Owner's Manual. It contains directions for maintaining the system, which should be scrupulously followed. Additional copies of this manual may be obtained by writing to Total Environmental Action, Inc., Church Hill, Harrisville, NH 03450.

NOTICE: Due to the complex nature of the designs in this manual, and due to the critical importance of the level of skill and responsibility on the part of the builder, neither T.E.A., Inc. nor Chilton, nor any of their employees makes any warranty, express or implied, in respect of (or assumes any legal liability or responsibility for) the accuracy, safeness, completeness, or usefulness of any information, apparatus, product design, or process disclosed, or represents that its use would not infringe upon privately owned rights.

CONTENTS

PREFACE

Americans had been accustomed to an unlimited supply of cheap energy until recent years. But in a short time, most of us have been shaken from our fool's paradise into the harsh reality of a finite and rapidly dwindling supply of fossil fuels. Spiraling prices, and in some cases rationing, have made the point: we need other sources of energy.

To compound the problem, we are increasingly aware of threats to our physical health and to our environment from new technological processes and applications and the indiscriminate use of energy. We are paying the price in a higher incidence of respiratory diseases and cancer, and in polluted air and water.

We need a solution to the dilemma. Nuclear power seems to offer at least a temporary solution to the energy shortage, but it exacerbates pollution and health problems. The consequences are still a subject of speculation and study, but one fact cannot be denied: for the first time in history, mankind is dramatically affecting the Earth in a way that is irreversible for tens of thousands of years, the time required for radioactive waste to decay. There is also growing agreement that nuclear power will be much more expensive than originally believed.

A partial answer to both problems is shining in our faces. Solar energy is a practical source for a large fraction of the country's heating requirement. By using the sun to heat buildings, we can begin to decrease our dependence on vanishing fossil fuels and reduce the use of polluting energy sources. Solar energy doesn't require transmission lines or pipelines, it produces no dangerous radioactive wastes, no black smoke, no black water, and it doesn't ravage the land with strip mines. The technology for solar home heating is simple, we have it now, and anyone with appropriate building experience can apply it.

Solar Heating: A Construction Manual provides complete plans and step-by-step instructions for building the MODEL-TEA Solar Heating System. It also contains a wealth of information on development of the design, solar basics, materials analysis, and engineering of solar systems. The MODEL-TEA solar system can be integrated into an existing or new building on site,

and performs as well as commercially manufactured systems,
but at roughly one-half the cost. On-site assembly allows for a
tremendous savings, since the building itself performs the function of many materials normally included in an installed, commercially manufactured collector panel.

The MODEL-TEA was developed through an intensive two-
year research and development project at Total Environmental
Action, Inc., supported in part by the United States Department
of Energy, Solar Heating and Cooling Research and Development Branch. The purpose was to create a design for an active
solar air-heating system which was economical, durable, attractive, and could be readily constructed by any experienced
builder. For maximum usefulness, the design had to be adaptable to either walls or roofs, and to new or existing buildings.
The need for such a system was clear. Commercially manufactured active systems for residential applications were too expensive to be cost-effective. Passive solar systems, though less
expensive, could not be easily integrated into many types of
buildings. T.E.A. believed that an inexpensive active solar
system could have a major nationwide effect on residential
energy use.

Solar technology and its applications are rapidly changing:
new materials and products become available and the economic frame of reference is unpredictable. Since new devel-
opments may directly affect decisions and choices presented in
this manual, it is important to maintain close contact with the
current state of the field. T.E.A. has a strong belief in the importance of site-built active solar to residential energy use, and will
endeavor to continue major research and development in this
vital area. At this point, however, a large part of the challenge
shifts to the consumer. This construction manual supports our
belief that the MODEL-TEA solar system works, is cost-effective,
and will provide an attractive option for many of the homes in
our country. You must make it happen—must dare to be the
first in your area, so your neighbors can see for themselves. We
need your comments, and your neighbor's comments. This book
offers one basic design, which is suitable to a wide variety of
needs, applications, and geographical areas. Necessarily, as in
any complex project, compromises had to be made. Perhaps,

for your particular application, you feel a design change is appropriate. We would appreciate any comments on design suggestions, problems, additions, or information that will help us to provide better site-built designs. We strongly urge you to send a stamped, self-addressed envelope to T.E.A. before you order materials and begin construction. Then T.E.A. can send you updated information on any materials or new products. Also, at that time we will send you a questionnaire to be filled out upon completion of your particular installation. Additional copies of the Owner's Manual which appears at the end of this book, as well as the construction drawings, are also available from T.E.A.

Many people at T.E.A. have contributed to the development of the MODEL-TEA design. Peter Temple had overall responsiblity for the preparation of this manual, and wrote the first three chapters and the background materials in the Appendixes. Jennifer Adams prepared the construction drawings, graphics, and wrote the chapters on step-by-step construction. The basic idea for the horizontal-flow air collector was conceived by Charles Michal in 1975, and the design was developed during two projects managed by Joseph Kohler and Peter Temple. They guided the work through the major design decisions and were responsible for the theoretical analysis, testing of prototypes and materials, analysis of experimental results, and system design. Jennifer Adams developed the collector construction details and assisted in the materials choices. Dan Lewis developed the specifics of air-handling system design, and Vic Reno prepared the control system diagrams. Charles Michal and Paul Sullivan made significant contributions to major design decisions, and Jeremy Coleman assisted in the initial development of the design.

Peter L. Temple
Jennifer A. Adams
Total Environmental Action, Inc.
Harrisville, NH 03450

SOLAR HEATING: A CONSTRUCTION MANUAL

INTRODUCTION

Solar power is becoming an attractive and sensible alternative to paying ever-increasing electricity, gas, and oil bills. There are many different ways one can use solar energy economically, and this manual shows how one particular type of system can be cost-effective. But the decision of whether or not to install a solar collector is complex, involving not only economic factors, but also aesthetic, ecological, and personal considerations.

Before this decision is made, some other aspects of solar should be discussed. It does not make sense to invest in solar energy for your home without first taking full advantage of energy conservation techniques. Most energy conservation measures are more cost-effective (shorter payback) than solar measures, and since putting heat into a house is so expensive, it should not be wasted. The house should be tight and well-insulated. In most areas of the country, walls should be insulated to R-19 (e.g., 6 in. of fiberglass) and ceilings to at least R-30. Windows should at least be double glazed and, in many areas, triple glazing is preferable. The foundation should be insulated, windows and doors weatherstripped, and a vapor barrier should be installed on the inside of all insulated surfaces. All these factors contribute to retaining whatever heat energy the building receives.

PASSIVE AND ACTIVE SYSTEMS

Once a house is made energy efficient, the simplest and most economical way to use solar energy is by direct gain, often referred to as "passive solar." Direct gain means letting the sun shine through windows; the sunlight heats whatever it strikes, and that heat is retained within the house (the greenhouse effect). New houses designed to take advantage of passive solar often have a long east-west dimension, most of the glazing on

FIG. 1 SITE-BUILT ACTIVE SOLAR INSTALLATION

the south wall, a few windows on the east and west, and hardly any on the north. A greenhouse attached to the south wall is a common application of direct gain. Passive solar systems can easily be integrated with contemporary designs for new homes, but not so easily with traditional designs or for retrofitting existing buildings.

Active systems, such as the MODEL-TEA, have a significant advantage in this regard. Since active systems consist of collectors which can be mounted on either a wall or roof, and delivery systems which can carry the heat to any part of the house or to remote storage, these systems can be easily integrated into any building that has a proper solar exposure. Existing homes frequently do not have sufficient space on the south wall for a reasonable size solar system, or may not even have good solar wall exposure, but they *may* have a large roof area exposed to the sun. Thus, what constitutes a difficult retrofit for a passive system is straightforward for an active system. New home designs can be traditional, without heavily glazed south walls, yet still have a large active solar system on a well-oriented roof. Active collectors can even be mounted on south walls, with the advantage that the wall is fully insulated and thus does not lose as much heat to the outside as direct-gain windows would.

While active systems lend themselves to easier building integration, they are usually more expensive than passive systems. The initial cost may not be much greater, but active systems have shorter lifetimes than passive systems. Commercially manufactured collectors cost roughly $25 to $30 per square foot (installed), and the added cost of controls, delivery system and storage bring the total installed cost to $50 or more per square foot of collector. Thus, a typical 400-square-foot commercial system might cost $20,000. Such a system is only marginally competitive at current fossil fuel prices.

The MODEL-TEA solar system differs substantially from these commercial systems. It is available at a tremendously lower cost because of its innovative design and because it is integrated into the building. The collector can be built for $7 to $11 per square foot, depending on choice of options, and the installed cost for a 400-square-foot system is roughly $8000. This is approximately one-half the cost of a manufactured system.

There are many criteria by which the economics of a solar installation may be judged, including cost, payback time, return on investment, benefit/cost ratios, and so on. Most methods require a prediction of fossil fuel costs many years into the future, leading to uncertain results which, at best, are only useful in defining limits. In Section 1.4, the cost of the MODEL-TEA System is studied in detail and found to be a very attractive economic option.

Few people will make the decision to install a solar system based on economics alone. Other factors should influence the decision: for instance, the security of having a totally dependable source of heat, free of fuel shortages and other unpredictable events. On a seasonal basis, the available solar energy is very predictable and probably more dependable than anything else in our world today. Another consideration is the ecological ramifications, the motivation to reduce consumption of nonrenewable fuels. A homeowner who uses a solar heating system has the satisfaction of conserving nonrenewable fuels so

---

they may be used in more appropriate applications. It is not sensible to waste a valuable and diminishing resource on home heating which can be accomplished just as effectively through solar. Finally, and perhaps most significant, solar energy does not pollute the air we must breathe, the water we must drink, nor the Earth where, for the foreseeable future, we must live. People who use active solar now know that they are the vanguard of a movement which will be not only highly beneficial, but perhaps essential, to our civilization.

There is a great deal of available information on solar energy, from both private and public sources. Books, magazines, and government organizations which can help acquaint the public with the rapidly growing solar field are listed in Appendix B.

DEVELOPMENT OF THE MODEL-TEA SYSTEM

The MODEL-TEA solar system was developed by Total Environmental Action, Inc. (T.E.A.) with partial support from the United States Department of Energy, Solar Heating and Cooling Research and Development Branch, Office of Conservation and Solar Applications. The concept of the project was to significantly lower the cost of active solar systems by: (1) designing a collector which shares several of its components with the building, reducing duplication of materials; and (2) developing a low-cost delivery and storage system. A collector built on site (site-fabricated) and properly integrated into the building also has the advantages of improved performance, due to decreased side and back losses, and improved visual appearance of the building.

A number of builders throughout the country have developed site-fabricated collector designs. Although many of these designs seem to work reasonably well, most have not been subjected to a careful analysis to determine if performance could be improved, durability increased, or cost reduced. Furthermore, construction plans for site-built collectors are usually incomplete, if they are available at all, and very little information is available on designs for delivery systems and storage.

The purpose of the T.E.A. endeavor was first to develop an attractive, durable, low-cost, site-built collector that would perform as well as commercially manufactured collectors, and that could be easily integrated into the majority of new or existing wood frame buildings. An additional goal was to design low-cost, effective air-handling and storage systems appropriate to the various potential collector applications. T.E.A. began by conducting a survey of site-built installations throughout the country to learn about the experiences of others. Information was compiled regarding specific collector designs, materials used, cost of construction, problems experienced and solutions developed. An investigation to determine the materials most suitable for use in a site-built collector was then undertaken. Glazings, absorber plates, paints, caulks, structural materials, and fasteners were evaluated, regarding such factors as performance, cost, durability, ease of handling, and availability.

Six collectors were designed, based on the results of the survey, the materials study, and T.E.A.'s previous experience with site-built collectors. These designs were rigorously analyzed. The theoretical efficiency was calculated and the annual energy output of each design was computed. Materials lists and construction estimates were completed to determine the installed cost of each design. The ease of construction, appearance, and durability of each design was assessed, and the best design was then selected.

Five collector test modules were constructed and tested according to strict industry test procedures (ASHRAE 93-77 standards and the HUD thirty-day stagnation test). The modules satisfactorily passed these tests. The results confirmed that the design selected was durable and provided performance comparable to manufactured collectors at less than one-half the cost. Once glass was chosen as the glazing material, another test was conducted to evaluate three different systems for mounting the glass on the collector. The result of this phase of the project was a thoroughly proven collector design. (For detailed information on the project development, see Appendix B.)

A similar philosophy governed the approach to the development of designs for the air-handling systems, controls and storage. After surveying current designs, T.E.A. began work on a simple, low-cost design which could be integrated into existing

FIG. 2 COLLECTOR TEST MODULE

buildings or used in new construction. This system is straight-forward to build and does not depend upon a particular build-ing configuration. T.E.A. also developed an innovative system design specifically for new buildings. This is an even more in-expensive design, but is only suitable for new construction where the building can be carefully designed to accommodate the solar system.

The final design, collector and sub-systems, was named the MODEL-TEA Solar Heating System. Like the famous automo-bile, it is a classic: durable, reliable, available at a low cost in the marketplace. To paraphrase Henry Ford, it can be painted any color you want, as long as it is black!

CHAPTER 1

THE MODEL-TEA SOLAR HEATING SYSTEM

The MODEL-TEA system consists of a solar collector, delivery and control system, and storage. The collector receives energy from the sun, which heats a black metal plate within the collector. Air is blown through the collector, becomes hot, and then is delivered to the living space of the house. The control system automatically governs the air flow according to the demand for heat and available sun. For large systems, a storage bin is provided. Then, when the collector is providing more heat than the living space requires, the surplus heat is sent to storage to be held in reserve for use at night or during periods of cloudy weather.

This general relationship of subsystems is similar to that of most commercial active solar systems. All solar systems use either a liquid (water or anti-freeze) or air to carry heat from the collector to the living space. Air was chosen as the heat-carrying medium for the MODEL-TEA system. Appendix B contains a complete discussion of this choice and of other decisions made in the design of this system. The most important difference between the MODEL-TEA and commercially available systems is that the MODEL-TEA is actually built on-site, fully integrated into the building structure, thus providing a tremendous savings in cost.

1.1 COLLECTOR

The MODEL-TEA collector is an air-type, flat-plate collector designed for installation on either pitched roofs or vertical walls in new or existing buildings. A perspective sketch of the roof version is shown in Figure 1.2. The major components of the collector are a glass cover system, a black-ribbed metal absorber plate, Thermo-ply building sheathing, and sheet-metal manifold pans located between the outer studs or rafters.

Sunlight passes through the glazing cover and is converted to heat on the black absorber plate. The glazing cover reduces losses to the outdoor air and the collector plate heats up. Air from the room or rock bin is ducted into the collector manifold pan, as indicated by the arrow at upper right in Figure 1.2. Air passes through the manifold openings in the sheathing and

THE MODEL-TEA
SOLAR HEATING SYSTEM

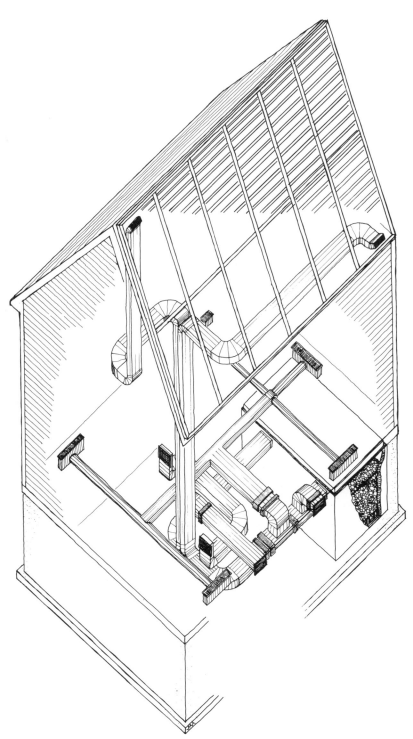

FIG. 1.1 COMPLETE MODEL-TEA SYSTEM

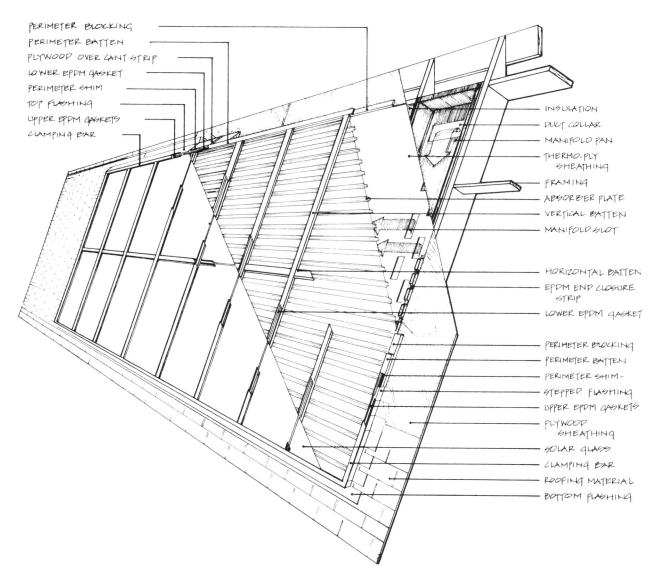

PERIMETER BLOCKING
PERIMETER BATTEN
PLYWOOD OVER CANT STRIP
LOWER EPDM GASKET
PERIMETER SHIM
TOP FLASHING
UPPER EPDM GASKETS
CLAMPING BAR

INSULATION
DUCT COLLAR
MANIFOLD PAN
THERMO-PLY SHEATHING
FRAMING
ABSORBER PLATE
VERTICAL BATTEN
MANIFOLD SLOT

HORIZONTAL BATTEN
EPDM END CLOSURE STRIP
LOWER EPDM GASKET

PERIMETER BLOCKING
PERIMETER BATTEN
PERIMETER SHIM
STEPPED FLASHING
UPPER EPDM GASKETS
PLYWOOD SHEATHING
SOLAR GLASS
CLAMPING BAR
ROOFING MATERIAL
BOTTOM FLASHING

FIG. 1.2 MODEL-TEA ROOF COLLECTOR

travels the length of the collector in the horizontal channels formed between the raised portion of the ribbed absorber and the sheathing. Heat is transferred from the absorber to the air, and heated air then passes through manifold openings into a manifold pan at the opposite end of the collector, and is returned to the room or a rock bin through air ducts. A blower is required to move the air through the system. Other components found in a complete system include rock bin storage, thermostatic controllers, and motorized dampers.

The construction of the MODEL-TEA collector is straightforward. The roof (or wall) is framed in the usual manner, horizontal blocking is added, and manifold blocking is installed. Sheet metal manifold pans are fastened between the rafters (or studs) at each end of the collector, as shown in Figure 1.2. For collectors longer than 26 feet, manifold pans are also located between the rafters on each side of the center rafter, as explained in Chapter 4. Caulking is applied generously all around the upper edge of the manifold pans. The Thermo-ply sheathing is attached to the roof (or wall), and all seams are carefully caulked. Manifold slots are cut in the sheathing. Blocking is fastened around the perimeter of the Thermo-ply.

The absorber plate is 8-inch ribbed, industrial aluminum siding, painted flat black. It is installed over the sheathing, extending to the outer manifold blocking. Then the ends are sealed with EPDM (ethylene propylene diene monomer) rubber end closure strips and a continuous caulk bead, and the top and bottom edges are caulked. Battens are fastened to the absorber plate. The glazing system is then attached: a single layer of glass on the roof version, and double glass on the wall collector. The collector is completed by installing flashing and aluminum glazing bars.

1.2 AIR-HANDLING AND CONTROL SYSTEMS

The air-handling system consists of fans, ductwork, automatic dampers, and controls which operate to deliver the heated air. If the collector is small, the house can usually receive all the heated air directly from the collector, eliminating the need for a

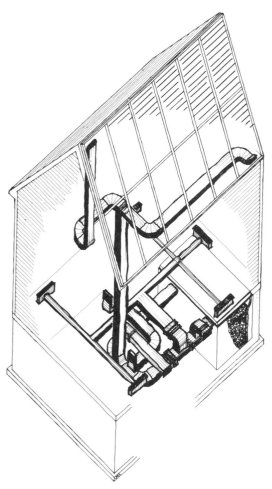

FIG. 1.3 AIR-HANDLING SYSTEM

storage bin. Then the required air-handling system is very
simple: it consists of one fan, with supply and return ductwork
between the collector and the living space. Whenever there is
sufficient sunshine and the living space is below the overheating
temperature, the controls turn on the fan.

A larger collector can usually deliver more heat to the living
space in the daytime than is necessary. In these systems, a
storage rock bin is used to hold the surplus heat for a later time,
such as at night, when it is needed. This type of full-scale installation is characterized by three air-handling modes: collector

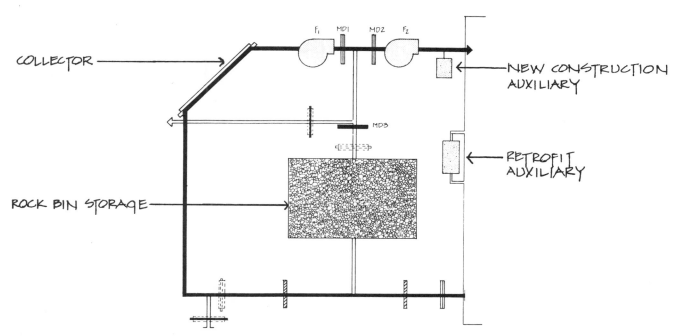

FIG. 1.4 COLLECTOR-TO-HOUSE MODE

to house, collector to storage, and storage to house (Figures 1.4
to 1.6). When the collector is producing useful heat and the
house concurrently requires heat, the first mode is activated.
Air from the house is drawn through the collector, heated, and
then delivered back to the house. If the collector heat is not
sufficient to totally fulfill the house need, the house temperature
continues to drop, and the second stage of the thermostat activates the auxiliary heating system. The collector-to-house mode
continues to operate as long as there is both a heating need and
the collector air temperature remains above a minimum set
temperature.

   The second mode, collector to storage, is engaged whenever
the collector is warmer (by 20°F) than the cool side of the rock
bin, and the house does not require heat. Air from the cool side
of the rock bin is drawn through the collector, heated, and then
returned to the hot side of the rock bin. If the collector air temperature drops to within approximately 4°F of the cool side of the
rock bin, this mode is halted.

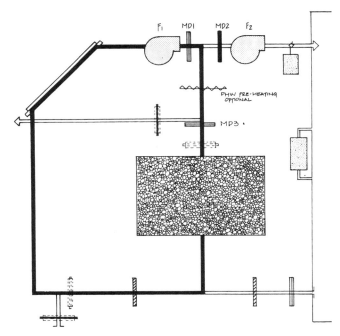

FIG. 1.5 COLLECTOR-TO-STORAGE MODE

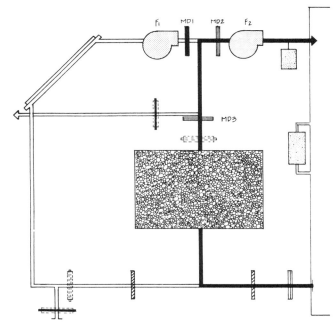

FIG. 1.6 STORAGE-TO-HOUSE MODE

The third mode, storage to house, operates when the house requires heat, but the collector is not hot enough to turn on. Air is drawn from the hot side of the rock bin, delivered to the house, and returned to the rock bin's cool side. If this heat is insufficient to meet the house need, the house temperature continues to drop, and the second stage of the thermostat activates the auxiliary heating system. The storage-to-house mode continues until either the house demand is satisfied or, in the case of retrofit, the air being delivered from the rock bin drops below 85°F.

The three-mode air-handling system uses two fans and three on/off dampers. It is assembled on-site from standard components and is suitable for either new construction or retrofitting to existing buildings. A water coil can be placed in the ductwork so the system may provide domestic hot water (DHW) in addition to space heating. The cost-effectiveness of the system is thereby increased, since it can provide useful service throughout the year.

T.E.A. also developed an innovative air-handling system which is suitable only for new construction. This is an even lower cost system, obtained by careful integration with the building design and the use of a different type of rock bin. This system is described in detail in Chapter 8.

1.3 STORAGE

Installations with sufficiently small collector areas (less than 200 square feet for retrofit and less than 150 square feet for new super-insulated houses), do not require storage. For larger collector areas, storage is essential to achieving efficient use of the collected heat. Storage for the MODEL-TEA system consists of an insulated box, or bin, filled with small rocks. The rocks have sufficient spaces (voids) between them so that air can be blown through the bin between duct connections on the two ends. As heated air from the collector is blown through the bin, heat is transferred from the air to the rocks, and the cooled air then returns to the collector to be reheated. There is good heat transfer from the air to the rocks, due to the large surface-to-volume

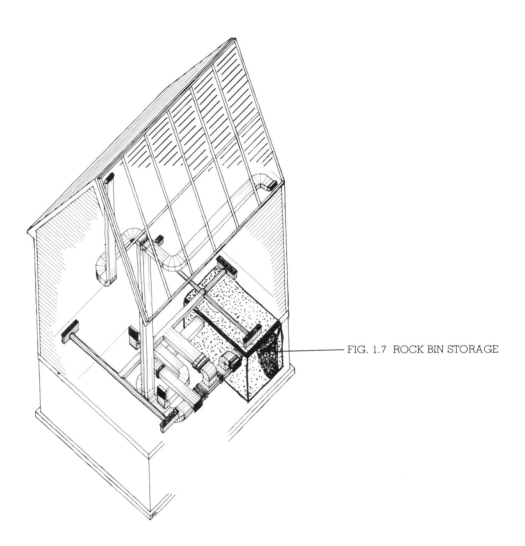

FIG. 1.7 ROCK BIN STORAGE

ratio of the rocks. In addition, rocks have the capacity to store a large amount of heat with only a moderate rise in temperature.

In the storage-to-house mode, air flows through the rock bin in the opposite direction. Cool house air is drawn into the cool side of the bin, heated by the rocks as it passes, and delivered from the hot side back to the house. Since air flow direction reverses, depending upon whether the rock bin is being charged or discharged, this type of storage is known as a two-way rock bin. Thermal stratification, the fact that the rock bin usually maintains a temperature difference between the two sides, is due to the relatively poor thermal conductivity of the rock-void combination.

The MODEL-TEA rock bin has a U-shaped air-flow path which allows both inlet and outlet duct connections to be made at the top of the bin, and limits the overall height. These are important features when retrofitting rock bins into existing basements where space may be tight. Rocks can usually be dumped into the bin on a chute through a basement window. For houses on slabs, the rock bin must be integrated into a space on the first floor. The rock bin is constructed on site from standard framing lumber, and lined with plywood and gypsum board. Joints are carefully caulked and taped to prevent air leakage and the bin is fully insulated. Chapter 8 contains a description of the one-way rock bed used in T.E.A.'s innovative system, suitable only for new construction.

1.4 COSTS

The MODEL-TEA Solar Heating System costs roughly one-half as much as a commercially manufactured solar system. Full-size residential air and liquid manufactured solar systems average $55 to $65 per square foot of collector, fully installed, whereas a large MODEL-TEA installation, complete with storage, costs approximately $23 per square foot. The MODEL-TEA roof collector, with single glass glazing, costs $7.05 per square foot installed for a 16 x 24-foot collector. A small wall version, with double glass panels, costs about $12.20 per square foot. These prices are conservative; they reflect small quantities of materials, purchased at high unit costs, and high labor estimates which assume no prior experience with building this type of design.

Cost figures are inevitably uncertain for many reasons. High inflation rates will cause dramatic increases in both the material and labor components of the final figure, and geographical lo-

cation can also have a significant impact on these numbers. In
addition, material costs vary depending upon source of supply
and quantities purchased. For most materials, purchasing in
sufficiently large quantities can reduce prices by at least 50%.
Contractors who build many solar systems can easily lower both
material and labor costs by buying large quantities of materials
and gaining familiarity with the design. On the other hand,
builders installing a single small system may incur higher costs.

Two methods have been used to estimate costs of collector
materials, and where the results differed, the higher value has
been taken. T.E.A. contacted manufacturers, distributors, and
dealers to determine current prices, and from this information
estimated material costs at approximately $5.67 per square foot
for the roof collector and $10.95 per square foot for the wall
version. The alternative method, using 1981 *Means Cost Data*[1],
and giving credit for building insulation, vapor barrier, sheathing, and roofing or siding (−$2.12 for roof and −$2.32 for wall),
results in collector material costs of $4.20 per square foot for the
roof collector and $7.76 per square foot for the wall version,
using 8-inch rib aluminum. T.E.A. carefully documented labor
times for some actual installations and, using a labor rate of $10
an hour, estimated labor costs for the two collectors at $3.50 per
square foot for the roof and $4.12 per square foot for the wall.
Thus, the total collector costs are approximately $7.05 per square
foot for the roof collector, and $12.20 or $12.75 per square foot for
the wall version, depending upon whether 8-inch or 4-inch rib
aluminum is used (the 4-inch rib results in greater waste of material in the given wall design).

Tables 1.1 through 1.5 present costs for different parts of the
MODEL-TEA Solar Heating System. Table 1.6 summarizes the
total costs for the entire system. The air-handling material costs
in Table 1.5 are estimates based upon typical costs of standard
products. These numbers will vary, depending upon the actual
item purchased. T.E.A. obtained an estimate from a heating
contractor for a sample retrofit installation. Though the ductwork and other materials could be estimated fairly accurately, a
large amount of uncertainty exists in the labor figure. The contractor estimated $1500 for labor, covering all air-handling and

[1] *Building Construction Cost Data*, Robert Snow Means Company, Inc., Duxbury,
MA.

control system installation. But it was explained that this figure
contained a large safety margin because this type of work was
unfamiliar; with experience, the estimate would come down by
$800 to $1000. Thus, at the end of part 1 in Table 1.5, a final cost
figure is given taking into account an $810 reduction in labor
cost.

Though the total costs of the MODEL-TEA Solar Heating System are given in Table 1.6, the question remains: How cost-
effective is it? It is clear that the MODEL-TEA is much less expensive than manufactured solar heating systems, but that does
not necessarily mean that it is an economically attractive option.
The question of cost-effectiveness can only be answered by
somehow comparing the solar system option with the cost of the
conventional alternative over the same period of time. This type
of analysis is referred to as life cycle costing. It is a complex
endeavor, because it must take into account not only the heat
output of the solar system, its initial cost, and the current cost of
the fossil fuel alternative, but it also must account for general
inflation, fuel inflation, down payment and the interest rate on
the solar system, discount rate, maintenance costs, resale value,
and other parameters. If an attempt is made to calculate life-
cycle costs over a term of 25 years, inflation rates, discount rates,
tax rates, and so on must be predicted 25 years into the future.
This cannot be done with much certainty.

Then, once these bold economic assumptions are made, there
are many measures of cost-effectiveness among which to
choose. One can use return-on-investment, cumulative solar
savings, or various types of payback definitions. The payback
period is basically the time it takes for the cost of the fuel saved
to equal the cost of the solar system. But there are various ways
of defining these costs, depending upon whether the calculation
accounts for inflation, interest earned on money not spent, mort-
gage rates, etc.

T.E.A. decided to use the f-Chart Method, by Beckman, Klein,
and Duffie (see References and Resources). This is available as
a computer program which does two basic calculations: (1) it
calculates the thermal performance of the solar system, based
on solar radiation, weather data, and collector physical parameters; and (2) performs a life-cycle economic costing based on the
input of all necessary economic parameters. This program was

run for two systems, a full-size roof collector with storage and
DHW, and a small wall collector with no DHW and only minimal
storage. Calculations were done for both of these systems in
each of 5 cities: Atlanta, Baltimore, Boston, Denver, and Sac-
ramento. Some of the results are summarized in Table 1.7. The
first four columns are based only upon the performance calculation and the initial cost of the solar system. The numbers in the
last two columns stem from the economic analysis. The first
represents a payback period given by f-Chart and defined as
the years until undiscounted fuel savings equals investment.
The second is the present worth of cumulative solar savings over
the 25-year period. According to these numbers, the MODEL-
TEA is cost-effective.

Many assumptions had to be made in order to run the f-Chart
analysis. T.E.A. chose numbers which were realistic and would
not necessarily favor the collector's performance. For example,
it was assumed that the house was very well-insulated, had
high internal heat gains, and that the roof collector was at a 45°
pitch, rather than the optimum. All of these assumptions may
tend to reduce the apparent annual performance of the system.
The specific system parameters are presented in Appendix B.4.
The following are some of the economic assumptions which
were made: roof collector cost = $23.66 per square foot, wall
collector = $18.65 per square foot, mortgage interest rate = 12%,
term = 25 yr., discount rate = 8%, inflation = 11%, fossil fuel cost
= $15 per million Btu, and fuel inflation = 15%. Again, it should
be remembered that since these economic parameters cannot
really be predicted for 25 years into the future, this entire economic analysis is highly questionable, and perhaps only useful
for setting limits.

THE MODEL-TEA
SOLAR HEATING SYSTEM

TABLE 1.1
MATERIALS COST FOR ROOF COLLECTOR

16′ x 24′ module (16′4½″ x 23′6½″ actual)

Material	Quantity	Unit Cost	Total Cost
Manifold pans 30 gauge (4½″ x 22½″ x 16′) including labor	2	$89.50	$179.00
Thermo-ply ⅛″ Blue Super Strength 4′ x 8′ sheets	12 sheets	7.00	84.00
8″-Rib industrial siding 49⅝″ x 23′	4 sheets (385 ft²)	1.04/ft²	400.00
EPDM End Closure Strips 40″ long	10 pieces	2.03	20.30
Urethane caulk	16 tubes	4.69	75.00
Flat black paint	2 gallons	28.00	56.00
Wood	70 FBM	0.35	24.50
Aluminum screws, boxes of 100			
#12 x 1¼″	8 boxes	15.80	126.36
#12 x 1½″	2 boxes	21.00	42.00
#12 x 2½″	1 box	34.50	34.50
Smoke bomb	5	1.00	5.00
6-mil poly vapor barrier	385 ft²	0.03	11.55
1″ Fiberglass board insulation	64 ft²	0.30	19.20
R-19 Fiberglass batt insulation	422 ft²	0.24	101.28
$3/16$″ x 34″ x 96″ Solar glass, bought in quantities of one case (42 panes per case)	16 panes, 22.67 ft²/each	28.78/pane (1.27/ft²)	460.48
CY/RO U.G.S. bought in standard 25′ lengths	9 pieces	48.50	437.00
Aluminum screws, boxes of 100 #12 x 1½″	3 boxes	21.00	63.00
Silicone caulk	2 tubes	6.50	13.00
Flashing 10″ x .019″	90 ft²	0.36/ft²	32.40

TOTAL: $2184.57
$/ft²: $5.67

TABLE 1.2
MATERIALS COST FOR WALL COLLECTOR

8′ x 16′ module (8′9″ x 15′10½″ actual)

Material	Quantity	Unit Cost	Total Cost
Manifold pans 30 gauge (4½″ x 22½″ x 8′) including labor	2	$ 45.50	$ 91.00
Thermo-ply ⅛″ Blue Super Strength 4′ x 8′ sheets	4 sheets	7.00	28.00
4″-Rib industrial siding 45⅝″ x 16′	3 sheets (176 ft²)	1.13/ft²	199.00
EPDM End Closure Strips 40″ long	6 pieces	2.03	134.00
Urethane caulk	8 tubes	4.69	37.50
Flat black paint	1 gallon	28.00	28.00
Wood	40 FBM	0.35	14.00
Aluminum screws #12 x 1¼″	4 boxes	15.80	63.20
#12 x 1½″	1 box	21.00	21.00
#12 x 2½″	1 box	34.50	34.50
Smoke bomb	5	1.00	5.00
1″ Fiberglass board insulation	50 ft²	0.30	15.00
R-19 Fiberglass batt	156 ft²	0.24	37.44
6-mil poly vapor barrier	156 ft²	0.03	4.68
$^3/_{16}$″ x 46″ x 96″ Insulated solar glass with ½″ air space, bought in quantities of one case (18 panels per case)	4 panels, 30.67 ft² each	139.86 (4.56/ft²)	559.44
Pre-shimmed glazing tape	1136 lf	0.06	68.16
CY/RO U.G.S. without the lower EPDM gasket, bought in standard 25′ lengths	3 pieces	30.70	92.10
Aluminum screws, boxes of 100 #12 x 1½″	1 box	21.00	21.00
Silicone caulk	1 tube	6.50	6.50
		TOTAL:	$1445.52
		$/ft²:	$10.95

TABLE 1.3
MATERIAL AND LABOR COST FOR ROCK BIN

Material	Price	384 ft³ of Rock		600 ft³ of Rock	
		Quantity	Total	Quantity	Total
Anchor bolts or spacers	$ 0.70 each	23	$ 16.10	26	$ 18.20
Sill sealer	0.10 lf	45.25	4.52	53.5	5.35
Stud wall	396.00 MFBM	0.318	125.93	0.340	134.64
Outer ½″ CDX	0.33/ft²	362	119.46	465	153.40
Bolts	0.60 each	20	12.00	20	12.00
Divider	396.00 MFBM	0.050	19.80	0.104	41.18
Lag screws	0.50 each	10	5.00	10	5.00
R-19 fiberglass batt (5½″)	0.25/ft²	362	90.50	465	116.25
Inner ½″ CDX	0.33/ft²	398	131.34	638	210.54
Gypsum board	0.14/ft²	258	36.12	290	40.60
Caulk	6.50/tube	1	6.50	1	6.50
Insulation, rigid	0.53/ft²	(2)150	111.30	(2)170	180.20
Block	1.01 each	88	88.88	132	133.32
Lath	0.40/ft²	150	60.00	232	92.80
Gravel	7.85 yd.³	17.5	137.38	27	211.95
Sensors	22.65 each	2	45.30	2	45.30
Pipe, collar, cap	4.84 each	2	9.68	2	9.68
Duct collar	12.00 each	2	24.00	2	24.00
Cover: lumber	384.00 MFBM	0.067	25.73	0.113	43.39
½″ CDX	0.33/ft²	123	40.59	193	63.69
gypsum board	0.14/ft²	(2)160	44.80	(2)253	70.84
1″ polystyrene	0.29/ft²	123	35.67	193	55.97
fiberglass batt (R-11, 3½″)	0.16/ft²	123	19.68	193	30.88
caulk	6.50/tube	3	19.50	3	19.50
gasket	0.53 lf	46	24.38	58	30.74
lag screws	0.63 each	29	18.27	35	22.05

	Total	$/ft³ (384 ft³)	Total	$/ft³ (600 ft³)
Materials	$1272	$3.31	$1778	$2.96
Labor	$1018	$2.65	$1442	$2.37
Total cost	$2290	$5.96	$3200	$5.33

TABLE 1.4
TOTAL COST FOR MODEL-TEA
COLLECTOR (per square foot)

	Materials	Siding Credit	Insulation & V.B. Credit	Labor	Total
Roof Collector single glazed with solar glass	$ 5.67	−1.30	−0.82	3.50	$ 7.05
Wall Collector double glazed with solar glass	$10.95	−1.79	−0.53	4.12	12.75

TABLE 1.5
MATERIAL AND LABOR COSTS FOR AIR-HANDLING SYSTEM AND CONTROLS

1. COMPLETE, FULL-SIZE SYSTEM (384 FT²):

	Quantity	Unit Cost	Total Cost
Motorized damper low leakage with low voltage motor	3	$156	$ 468
Blowers with motor and drive	2	184	368
Controls			
relays	3	10	30
thermostat	1	30	30
differential controller	1	60	60
heating and power venting sensors	2	1 @ 20	20
		1 @ 25	25
Miscellaneous			60
Overheating alarms #1 Alarm			
transformer	1	6	6
switch	1	2	2
alarm	1	12	12
sensor	1	25	25

TABLE 1.5, Continued
MATERIAL AND LABOR COSTS FOR AIR-HANDLING SYSTEM AND CONTROLS

1. COMPLETE, FULL-SIZE SYSTEM (384 FT²), continued

	Quantity	Unit Cost	Total Cost
#2 Alarm			
power source/battery backup	1	80	80
switch	1	2	2
alarm	1	12	12
sensor	1	25	25
Ductwork			1080
estimate obtained for sample retrofit system (worst case)		Subtotal	$2305
DHW			
60-gallon tank	1		270
hot water coil	1		250
10 GPM pump	1		113
controller and sensors	1		72
plumbing valves	1		120
		Subtotal	$ 825
Labor			1750
professional estimate obtained on sample retrofit system for all controls and air handling (may be reduced by $810 by experience)			−810
		Subtotal	$ 940
		TOTAL	$4070.00
		$/ft²	$ 10.60

2. WALL COLLECTOR SYSTEM, NO STORAGE (132 FT²):

	Quantity	Unit Cost	Total Cost
Blower	1		85
Controls	1		120
Ductwork	1		180
Labor	1		350
#1 Alarm	1		45
		TOTAL	$ 780.00
		$/ft²	$ 5.90

TABLE 1.6
MODEL-TEA SYSTEM COSTS

1. COMPLETE SYSTEM, 384 FT² ROOF COLLECTOR, WITH STORAGE AND DHW:

	Cost	$/ft²
Collector	$2770	$ 7.10
Rock bin	1690	5.96
System	3660	10.60
	$7920	$23.66/ft²

2. WALL COLLECTOR, 132 FT², NO STORAGE:

Collector	2660	12.75
System	620	5.90
	$2880	$18.65/ft²

TABLE 1.7
F-CHART COMPUTER SIMULATIONS OF MODEL-TEA PERFORMANCE AND COST

1. ROOF COLLECTOR, 45°, 350 ft², STORAGE AND DHW

	Solar* Fraction (%)	MBtu/yr	Btu/ft²/yr	Initial Cost$/MBtu/yr	Payback† Period (yr)	Cumulative Solar Savings ($)
Atlanta	63	28.5	81,500	290	10	$ 7380
Baltimore	45	30.8	87,900	269	10	9170
Boston	36	28.8	82,200	288	10	7590
Denver	69	58.6	167,500	141	7	31,900
Sacramento	69	27.7	79,200	299	10	6730

2. WALL COLLECTOR, 160 ft², 90°, NO DHW

	Solar* Fraction (%)	MBtu/yr	Btu/ft²/yr	Initial Cost$/MBtu/yr	Payback† Period (yr)	Cumulative Solar Savings ($)
Atlanta	52	8.26	51,600	361	11	$ 1010
Baltimore	33	9.53	59,600	313	11	2040
Boston	25	8.78	54,900	340	11	1440
Denver	57	21.57	134,800	138	7	11,860
Sacramento	64	7.99	49,900	373	12	800

*Solar Fraction: percent of total load supplied by the solar system.

†Payback Period: number of years until undiscounted fuel savings equals investment.

CHAPTER 2

NEW CONSTRUCTION AND RETROFIT

Energy conservation is essential to good solar home design; an active or passive solar heating system is chosen only after energy conservation measures have been employed. The basic idea, after all, is simply to let sunlight in through windows and keep it there, whether those windows are called collectors or not. So, the first consideration is keeping energy in the house.

In new construction, energy conservation begins with siting considerations, such as protection from prevailing winds and use of a southern slope, including building into a hill. The next step is the overall building design, taking into account an east-west elongation, natural flow of heat through the structure, natural summer ventilation, air-lock entries, and natural lighting. Any building in a climate cold enough to warrant an active solar heating system should be well insulated. In such areas this means a minimum of R-19 wall insulation, and ceiling insulation from R-30 to R-38 for colder regions. Windows should be at least double glazed, and triple glazed in more northern regions. In areas with significant cooling loads (very warm summers), these measures will provide major summertime savings as well. Foundations or slabs should be insulated, windows and doors should be tight, and a complete polyethylene vapor barrier should be used. All of these factors contribute to retaining whatever heat energy the building gains.

Retrofitting energy conservation measures to existing buildings is usually more difficult than dealing with new construction, but still a great deal can be done. Cellulose insulation can be blown into uninsulated wall cavities, attics can be readily insulated, and storm windows and weatherstripping are easily installed. Polyethylene vapor barriers are probably not feasible, but in most cases two coats of vapor barrier paint and appropriate caulking will suffice. There is much information available on energy conservation measures; the homeowner should consult governmental energy offices and local bookstores.

Direct gain, or passive solar, is the simplest and most cost-effective means of transferring solar energy into a house. Windows, which exist for other reasons, can be employed as solar "collectors" by giving consideration to orientation to the sun and shading. If the windows are sealed with insulating shutters at night, they become even more efficient solar collectors. However, if too much area is devoted to windows, energy may be

FIG. 2.1   SOLAR HOME UNDER CONSTRUCTION,

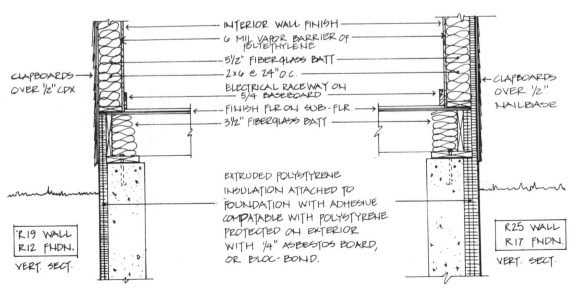

INTERIOR WALL FINISH
6 MIL VAPOR BARRIER OF POLYETHYLENE
5½" FIBERGLASS BATT
2×6 @ 24" O.C.
ELECTRICAL RACEWAY ON 5/4 BASEBOARD
FINISH FLR ON SUB-FLR.
3½" FIBERGLASS BATT

CLAPBOARDS OVER ½" CDX

CLAPBOARDS OVER ½" NAILBASE

EXTRUDED POLYSTYRENE INSULATION ATTACHED TO FOUNDATION WITH ADHESIVE COMPATABLE WITH POLYSTYRENE PROTECTED ON EXTERIOR WITH ¼" ASBESTOS BOARD, OR BLOC-BOND.

R19 WALL
R12 FNDN.
VERT. SECT.

R25 WALL
R17 FNDN.
VERT. SECT.

FIG. 2.2 EXTERIOR INSULATION AND SHEATHING

collected at a higher rate than it is needed, and overheating will result. Then there must be a means for storing that surplus heat for a time when it will be useful. This storage can be accomplished by having the direct sunshine fall on slate, stone, tubes of water, or any other material which has a high capacity for storing heat. When the room temperature falls, the heat will be radiated from the storage materials back to the living space. In new construction, it is often possible to design a building so that the majority of the heating requirement can be supplied through direct gain.

When using south-facing windows, it is important to remember that the gross building heating requirement increases along with solar aperture area. If night insulation and thermal mass

FIG. 2.3   COLLECTOR UNDER CONSTRUCTION

are not employed, the optimum window area may be surprisingly small, particularly in cold climates without a great deal of sun. Double-glazed windows will lose heat at rougly ten times the rate of a well insulated wall, so it definitely does not pay to have large areas of glass without night insulation and added thermal storage capacity. Energy conservation measures and proper application of passive solar systems, such as direct gain, are the first steps to be taken: they are the most economical. Once these principles have been applied, there is a definite role for a cost-effective active solar system.

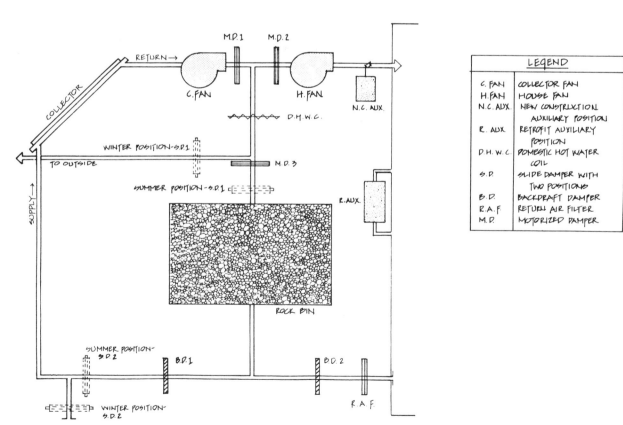

FIG. 2.4 LEGEND FOR MODEL-TEA CONSTRUCTION SCHEMATICS

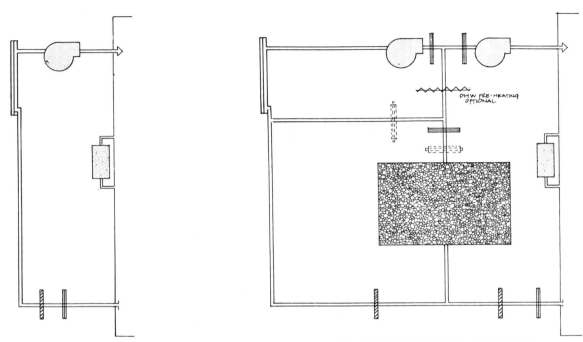

FIG. 2.5 RETROFIT: WALL COLLECTOR
WITHOUT STORAGE SYSTEM

FIG. 2.6 RETROFIT: WALL COLLECTOR
WITH STORAGE SYSTEM

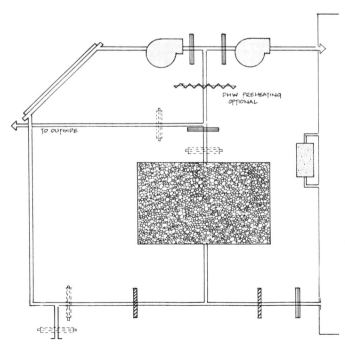

FIG. 2.7 RETROFIT: ROOF COLLECTOR WITH STORAGE

2.1 COLLECTOR SELECTION

The MODEL-TEA collector requires a wall or roof with a southern exposure. The collector may face 10° to either side of true south without a significant decrease in performance, and deviations up to 25° will probably result in only a 5% to 10% decrease. But performance drops off quickly for deviations greater than 30°. The first step in planning for the collector is to assess the building for suitable wall or roof locations. The collector not only requires proper southern orientation, but it should not be significantly shaded by any nearby trees or buildings. Since the sun is at the lowest angle in December, that angle should be determined for your geographical latitude and used to check the proposed collector location for full wintertime exposure. Partial summer shading by deciduous trees will not prevent adequate production of solar domestic hot water (DHW), since the collector area will be larger than necessary for that function.

The optimum tilt for the roof collector is latitude plus 15°. However, the pitch can vary by 10° without a significant effect, and even a variation of up to 20° will not decrease performance by more than 10%. In new construction the optimum pitch can be easily planned, but in retrofit applications a slight compromise may be required. In any roof application, there should be enough area available to accommodate a full-sized collector. The optimum size is determined primarily by economics; it ranges roughly from 350 ft² for small houses to over 500 ft² for large ones. For conventionally designed houses, it is often convenient and appropriate to use the entire available roof surface. This type of installation will be much more expensive than a small wall collector, since not only is the collector area larger, but storage and a complete air-handling system are required. The estimated costs are given in Section 1.5. A complete roof collector system combined with direct gain on the south wall is the best way to achieve a high solar fraction of total heating requirement.

The choice of wall or roof site will affect the size of the collector. For most single-family houses, a wall application of the MODEL-TEA does not allow a collector area of more than 200 ft². On the other hand, most roof applications allow as large a collector as is economically feasible—usually 350 to 500 ft² for moderate size houses. In new construction the collector can be carefully integrated into the building design, along with passive solar systems, so the size restrictions are more flexible. But in retrofit situations, and new houses of traditional design, those size limits apply.

If a wall collector is much less than 150 to 200 ft², and the building is reasonably large, it is not usually cost-effective to install a rock storage bin and the accompanying three-mode air-handling system. Most of the time, the building will be able to use all the heat directly available from the collector. The appropriate approach is to use a simple fan-and-duct delivery system to the living space, and the collector operates whenever there is sufficient sunshine and a concurrent demand for heat. This type of installation is very inexpensive, the only cost being the collector, one fan, and simple controls and ductwork. Since the wall collector is vertical, it does not require power venting in the summer. An attractive retrofit option exists when a building has a windowless south-facing wall that is not adjacent to a living space, such as a garage or storage room wall. This presents a perfect opportunity for a wall collector with a simple delivery system direct to the living space.

2.2 AIR-HANDLING AND STORAGE OPTIONS

If a small collector (less than 150 to 200 ft²) is used, the air-handling system becomes very simple. But if a full-size collector is selected, a number of options are available. First, consider new construction. When designing a new building, it is possible to integrate a full-sized collector into either the roof or, in the case of less traditional designs, the wall. Power venting will not be required for vertical wall collectors; for roof collectors, it will. In either case, a complete air-handling and storage system is needed, and this can be either the conventional system or the innovative system. The innovative system is potentially less expensive, but is more critically dependent upon precise sizing and engineering, and requires extensive integration with the building design. The innovative system should not be employed unless the services of an experienced solar designer are avail-

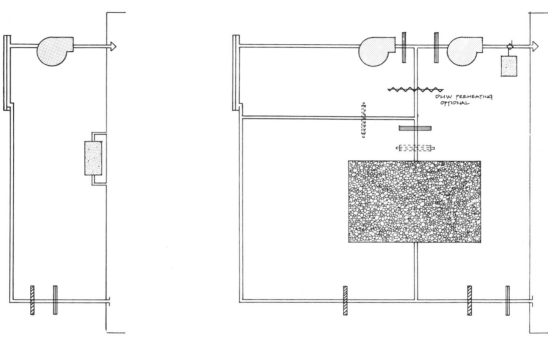

FIG. 2.8 NEW CONSTRUCTION: WALL COLLECTOR
WITHOUT STORAGE SYSTEM

FIG. 2.9 NEW CONSTRUCTION: WALL COLLECTOR
WITH STORAGE

able. The conventional system is more flexible in terms of building integration, and since it is a more common design, the costs can be predicted with greater certainty. With either system type, in new construction the auxiliary will be in series with the solar system, and the accompanying controls will assure maximum solar utilization by having the auxiliary draw solar preheated air.

In retrofit applications, only the conventional air-handling system is appropriate. This system can be integrated into any building where space can be found for the rock bin and air-handling equipment. If the building has a basement, the rock bin, air handler, and ductwork should be located there, in a position convenient to both the collector and living space. The rock bin should be located so that it may be readily filled, perhaps near a window so the rocks can be dumped in through a chute. All the ductwork to the living space can be located in the basement since the solar-heated air need only be delivered to the first floor. Second-floor heating requirements can be met, if necessary, with through-the-ceiling grills or a zoned auxiliary. In slab-built houses, the rock bin and air handler must be integrated into the first floor, and the ductwork fitted into the ceiling.

The auxiliary heating system will be in parallel with the solar system in all retrofit applications. This allows the solar system to be integrated into the building, regardless of the type of existing heating system. The accompanying controls are carefully designed to allow solar system air to be delivered to the house whenever both the house thermostat calls for heat and the solar-heated air is above 85°F. If more heat is required, it is provided by the auxiliary heating system simultaneously. If the collector air temperature drops below 85°F, but is still more than 20°F warmer than the cool side of the rock bin, then the collector air flow is diverted from the house to the rock bin. The auxiliary

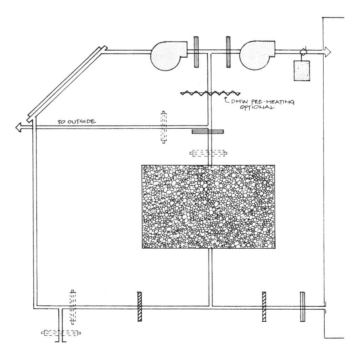

FIG. 2.10 NEW CONSTRUCTION: ROOF COLLECTOR WITH STORAGE

continues to heat the house. This control scheme achieves maximum utilization of solar in retrofit situations.

Wall collectors in retrofit applications will usually be small, perhaps no more than 200 ft². Installations of this size do not require storage and, of course, do not need power venting. Roof collectors always require power venting.

Domestic Hot Water Supply

A water coil can be inserted into the ductwork in any application of the MODEL-TEA in order to obtain domestic hot water (DHW). However, this is not an attractive option for wall collectors of moderate size or smaller. Vertical collectors receive less summertime solar radiation than roof collectors, and even less with smaller collectors. During the heating season a small wall collector can be well utilized for heating only; a DHW option would probably not increase the system's cost effectiveness. The DHW option adds a major expense to the total installation cost since, in addition to the coil, it requires a preheat tank, pump, valves, extra plumbing, and controls. A typical cost for the materials, including the tank, is roughly $825, and the labor for installation could add as much as another $700.

For roof collectors or any large collector, the DHW option is very attractive. The extra cost of the coil, controls, tank, and installation is significant, but the cost-effectiveness of the system is improved by allowing useful year-long operation. Summertime operation for DHW does not negate the need for power venting of roof collectors. Power venting is a requirement, while DHW is an option. But for all full-size systems, the DHW option is definitely recommended.

It is important that the DHW coil be located in the rock bin duct, as is shown in Figure 2.4. If, instead, the coil were placed in the collector return duct, it could freeze during the storage-to-house mode if motorized damper 1 were to leak. During nighttime storage-to-house heating, cold air would be pulled down from the collector through the coil. But located correctly, as shown, warm rock bin air is pulled through the coil in this mode.

Backdraft Dampers

Dampers allow the passage of air in only one direction and require no external control. There are two backdraft dampers shown in Figure 2.4. The purpose of these dampers is to prevent air leakage into the ductwork; if the duct system were airtight and the control dampers were leakproof, then the backdraft dampers would be unnecessary. However, since backdraft dampers are not expensive, it makes sense to install them as a precautionary measure. These dampers can be either purchased or site-fabricated (see Appendix A).

Power Venting

Tilted collectors are vented in the summer by drawing outside air through the collector and returning it to the outside. The ducts to the outside are opened in the spring, at the end of the heating season, by manually moving the two slide dampers shown in Figure 2.4. When the heating season begins, the two slide dampers are returned to their winter position, and carefully sealed. It is extremely important that the dampers be perfectly sealed so that there is absolutely no leakage from the outside during the heating season. Not only can outside air leakage have a devastating effect on overall system efficiency, but any leakage past slide damper 1 can directly affect the hot water coil. The slide dampers may either be purchased, or site-built as shown in Figure 2.11.

If the power venting system were to malfunction, or if it were not properly turned on by the homeowner at the end of the heating season, collector temperature could exceed acceptable limits (200°F). A high-temperature alarm is included in the design to warn the homeowner of such an event. For extra protection, there are two alarms, one set to trigger at 200°F and the other at 210°F.

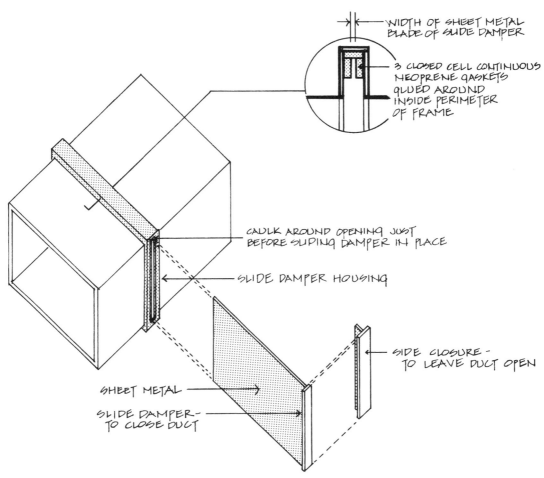

WIDTH OF SHEET METAL
BLADE OF SLIDE DAMPER

3 CLOSED CELL CONTINUOUS
NEOPRENE GASKETS
GLUED AROUND
INSIDE PERIMETER
OF FRAME

CAULK AROUND OPENING JUST
BEFORE SLIDING DAMPER IN PLACE

SLIDE DAMPER HOUSING

SIDE CLOSURE -
TO LEAVE DUCT OPEN

SHEET METAL

SLIDE DAMPER -
TO CLOSE DUCT

FIG. 2.11 SITE-FABRICATED SLIDE DAMPER

CHAPTER 3

SIZING, ENGINEERING, AND MATERIALS

3.1 COLLECTOR

Once a wall or roof collector has been decided upon, the size is largely determined by the building. On conventional buildings the collector will usually use almost all available space. Wall collectors will probably be limited to 200 ft² or less, and roof collectors will use the entire available roof area, perhaps 350 to 500 ft². A standard rule-of-thumb is that the collector area should equal one-fifth to one-quarter the floor area in southern climates and one-quarter to one-third the floor area in the north.

From a performance standpoint, the optimum area for a full-size installation depends upon the heating load of the house, collector performance, collector and air-handling system costs, controls, and storage. Whereas the cost of the collector is proportional to area, the remainder of the system contains a large fixed-cost base. A system with a small collector area requires almost the same expenditure for the air handler as one with a large collector. Thus, the total system cost per square foot of collector is higher for a small system. However, if the collector area is too large, it supplies more heat than can be used effectively.

If a more exact calculation of optimum collector size or expected performance is desired, a more sophisticated method can be used. *Solar Heating Design by the f-Chart Method*, by Klein, Beckman, and Duffie, describes one of the best available methods for performance calculations. The f-Chart program calculates useful output of the collector system, given the heating load, climate, and basic characteristics of the collector arrangement. The book explains how to do a calculation of the performance yourself. A computer calculation and a more detailed analysis can be obtained by contacting a solar engineering consulting firm. There are a number of such companies, including T.E.A., Inc., which will provide this service.

Air Flow Rate

The efficiency of air solar-heating systems depends on the air flow rate through the collector. As the air flow rate through a collector is increased, the collector efficiency increases. This increase in the collector efficiency results from two factors: (1) an increase in air velocity which increases the heat transfer rate from the absorber plate to the air; and (2) a decrease in the average air temperature in the collector. Increasing the air flow rate through the collector also increases the pressure drop through the collector, the air distribution system, and the rock storage bed as a direct result of increased air velocities. This requires larger air blowers. Although this energy is converted to useful heat, it increases operating costs if the cost of electricity is greater than the cost of fuel used for auxiliary heating.

For any system there is an optimum air flow rate at which the net energy savings is maximized. This flow rate depends on the climate, the length of the absorber plate, the size of the flow channels, and the design of the air distribution system and rock-bed. The optimum flow rate for the MODEL-TEA is approximately 2.5 CFM/ft² (cubic feet per minute, per square foot of collector). Table 3.1 gives air flow rates, along with other basic sizing information for collector areas from 200 to 500 ft². For collector areas less than 200ft², use 3 CFM/ft².

Manifold Pan Sizing

The manifolds must be designed to handle the air flow rate through the collector without an excessive pressure drop. It is recommended that the velocity of air in the manifold should not exceed 1000 FPM (feet per minute). The minimum manifold cross-sectional area is determined by dividing the total air flow rate between two manifolds by 1000; the minimum width of the manifold pans is determined by dividing the cross-sectional area by the depth of the manifolds.

Example 1: Determine the size of the manifold pans for a roof collector 20 feet long, 16 feet high, with manifolds located at each end of the collector. The collector area is 320 ft², so the total air flow rate would be 2.5 CFM/ft² x 320 ft² = 800 CFM. The minimum manifold cross-sectional area is therefore 800 CFM ÷ 1000 FPM = 0.80 ft² or 115 in.².

The interior cross-sectional area equals the depth of the pan times the width of the pan. The depth of the pan depends on the depth of the rafters, and on the amount of rigid insulation installed behind the pan, minus the thickness of the pan material (if other than 30 gauge sheet metal is used).

For instance, if the rafters were 2 x 10s (actual depth, 9¼ in.) and a minimum of 1 in. of rigid insulation is called for behind the pan, the pan depth would be 8¼ in. Divide 8¼ in. into the cross-sectional area of the pan, 115 in.² The result would be the width of the pan, in this case 14 in. If 2 in. of rigid insulation were used behind the pan, the pan depth would be 7¼ in., and the pan width would be approximately 16 in.

Example 2: Determine the manifold pan size for a wall collector 20 feet long and 8 feet high. The collector area is 160 ft², so the total air flow rate from Table 3.1 is approximately 500 CFM (for a small wall collector, less than 200 ft², a flow rate of 3 CFM/ft² is better than 2.5 CFM/ft²). The minimum manifold cross-sectional area is therefore 500 CFM ÷ 1000 FPM = 0.50 ft², or 72 in.²

If the wall studs are 2 x 6s (actual depth, 5½ in.) and 1 in. of rigid insulation were used behind the pan, the pan depth would be 4½ in. Dividing this depth into the cross-sectional area, 72 in.², yields 16 in. If 2 in. of rigid insulation were used, a preferred approach, the pan depth would be 3½ in., yielding a minimum pan width of 20½ in.

3.2 STORAGE

The two major engineering concerns when sizing a rock bin are the volume of rocks, and the pressure drop of the air as it flows through the rocks. A rule-of-thumb for rock bin volume is to provide roughly .75 cubic feet of rock for each square foot of collector area. This rule is flexible; some designers use slightly less and others use slightly more. The optimum size depends to a large extent on the volumetric flow rate of collector air through the rock bin. Too small a rock bin coupled with too much volumetric air flow would mean that the collector heat would be quickly "washed" through the rock bin, eliminating stratification and raising average collector temperatures. This reduces effi-

FIG. 3.1 ROCK BIN INSTALLATION FOR HEAT STORAGE

ciency since the outlet of the rock bin is the inlet to the collectors. The rule-of-thumb for the MODEL-TEA volumetric air flow rate is to provide 2.5 CFM of air per square foot of collector area. This should provide satisfactory rock bin stratification and solar energy storage, hence insuring good system performance.

Pressure drop is the other main concern; too much pressure drop means excessive fan power is required to force air through the rocks, and too little pressure drop might mean that the air will channel through the bin, creating hot spots, rather than spreading across the face of the rocks in the plenum and then flowing evenly through the bin. Pressure drop is a function of rock size, how tightly the rocks are packed (% voids), the velocity of air through the rocks (face velocity), and the length of the path presented to air flow. Rock size should be roughly ¾ in. to 1½ in. in diameter. It is not required that rocks be perfect spheres; irregularities found in crushed rock are acceptable.

When placed in the bin, the rocks should have approximately 40% to 50% voids: on the average, every cubic foot is roughly half solid rock and half air space by volume. This can be tested by filling a 55-gallon drum with rocks and then measuring how much water can be added before overflow occurs. If 22 gallons of water can be added, then this implies 40% voids; if 27½ gallons can be added, this implies 50% voids. With ¾ in. to 1½ in.-diameter rock and 40% to 50% voids, it is desirable to limit air velocities through the rocks to 20–30 FPM face velocities to avoid excessive pressure drops. This number is the volumetric air flow rate divided by the cross-sectional area of rocks presented to the air flow. The pressure drop in the rock bin is directly proportional to the path length of the air flow through the rocks; twice the path length implies twice the total pressure drop.

The MODEL-TEA system incorporates a U-shaped rock bin since that is an effective way to permit both the inlet and outlet duct connections to be made at the top of the rock bin and to limit the overall height. The height of the rock bin can be limited to 6′6″ overall if the rock height in each half of the bin is limited to 3′8″.

Using .75 ft³ of rock per square foot of collector area, ¾ in. to 1½ in. diameter rocks with 40% to 50% voids, 2.5 CFM per square foot collector, and a path length of 2 x 3′8″ (7.3 ft) will result in a rock bed with a satisfactory volume and pressure

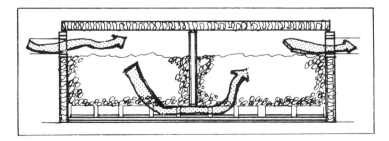

FIG. 3.2 AIR FLOW THROUGH A U-SHAPED ROCK BIN

drop (roughly .15" H₂O). Table 3.1 gives rock bin volumes for collector areas from 200 to 500 ft². Dividing the rock bin volume by 3.67 ft (rock height) will yield the cross-sectional area of rocks, and using this area the two horizontal dimensions can be determined.

3.3 AIR-HANDLING SYSTEM

The air-handling system should be installed by someone experienced in this type of work. A heating contractor or experienced solar installer should be able to easily site-build the system using the information in this book. The necessary engineering information has been developed according to collector area and is presented under Pre-Engineered Systems. That discussion and Tables 3.1, 3.2, and 3.3 present all the important sizing information. The following subsections on Air Supply, Blowers, and Ductwork provide important background information and the reasoning behind some of the engineering decisions.

Pre-Engineered Systems

Once the collector area is known, Tables 3.1 to 3.3 can be used to size the rock bin and to specify the collector and house blowers, the DHW coil (if used), the main ductwork dimensions, and the required supply register free outlet area. These tables were created by assuming three different collector areas of 200, 300, and 400 ft² and specifying the other system components to be compatible at these collector areas. The required length of ductwork for these systems was determined using an assumed retrofit system on a two-story house (see Figure 1.1). For determining blower requirements, the ductwork pressure drop was allowed to vary from ½ to 2 times the calculated value, since actual ductwork layouts can be expected to vary considerably. The collector, rock bin, and coil pressure drops remained constant as these are not a function of duct length.

As the collector area is decreased from the largest size in each of the given ranges in the chart, the following adjustments should be made in the system components:

TABLE 3.1
PRE-ENGINEERED SYSTEMS SIZING

Collector Area	System CFM *	Rock Bin Volume (rocks)†	Round Duct Size for Equivalent‡	Rectangular Duct Size (rounded up to nearest even DIM)	FPM	P_{loss}/100 ft of duct (in. H_2O)	Two Row DHW Coil Face Area (ft²)	P_{loss} thru DHW Coil	Free Area Supply Register Size (ft²)
200	500	150	11.0	8"x14"	760	.08	1.5	.10	5
225	563	169	11.4	8"x14"	780	.08	2	.10	5.6
250	625	188	11.9	8"x16"	800	.08	2	.10	6.3
275	688	206	12.4	8"x18"	830	.08	2	.11	6.9
300	750	225	12.8	8"x18"	840	.08	2.25	.10	7.5
325	813	244	13.6	8"x22"	800	.07	2.5	.10	8.1
350	875	263	14.0	8"x22"	820	.07	2.5	.12	8.8
375	938	281	14.5	8"x24"	820	.07	3	.10	9.4
400	1000	300	14.6	8"x24"	850	.07	3	.10	10.0
425	1063	319	15.2	8"x26"	850	.07	3	.12	10.1
450	1125	338	15.2	8"x26"	900	.08	3	.13	11.3
475	1188	356	15.6	8"x28"	900	.08	3	.15	11.9
500	1250	375	15.9	8"x30"	900	.07	3	.16	12.5

*At intermediate areas, use collector area x 2.5.

†Divide RB volume by 3.67 ft to get plan cross-sectional area of rocks in rock bin.

‡At intermediate areas, use next larger value. Other rectangular ducts which are equivalent can be found from Table 3.3 by entering the round duct equivalents.

TABLE 3.2
BLOWER SPECIFICATIONS AND SAMPLE REQUIREMENTS

	Collector Area		
	200–300 SF$_C$	301–400 SF$_C$	401–500 SF$_C$
Collector Blower	750 CFM @ $\frac{1}{2}$″–$\frac{3}{4}$″ P $\frac{2}{5}$″–$\frac{2}{3}$″ P*	1000 CFM @ $\frac{3}{5}$″–$\frac{4}{5}$″ P $\frac{1}{2}$″–$\frac{3}{4}$″ P*	1250 CFM @ $\frac{2}{3}$″–1″ P $\frac{1}{2}$″–$\frac{4}{5}$″ P*
Example	FGP 10-6A† BD 10-6A‡ BC 122§	FGP 12-6A BD 12-6A BC 122	FGP 12-6A BD 12-6A BC 150
House Blower	750 CFM @ $\frac{3}{10}$″–$\frac{6}{10}$″ P $\frac{1}{5}$″–$\frac{1}{2}$″ P*	1000 CFM @ $\frac{1}{4}$″–$\frac{3}{5}$″ P $\frac{1}{5}$″–$\frac{1}{2}$″ P*	1250 CFM @ $\frac{3}{8}$″–$\frac{7}{16}$″ P $\frac{1}{5}$″–$\frac{1}{2}$″ P*
Example	FGP 10-6A BD 10-6A BC 122	FGP 12-6A BD 12-6A BC 122	FGP 12-6A BD 12-6A BC 135

NOTE: For new systems with series auxiliary, supply ductwork and house blower are determined from the auxiliary CFM and air temperature delivery requirements necessary to meet design heat loss conditions. All blower motors should have internal thermal cutouts.

P = Pressure drop   ‡BD Lau blower (forward curved)
*Without DHW coil   §BC Bayley blower (backward inclined)
†FGP Lau blower (forward curved)

Example of System Sizing: Assume a roof collector 16 ft x 24 ft with the DHW option (384 ft²): Looking at Tables 3.1 and 3.2, we find:
  a) Rockbin rock volume: $\frac{3}{4}$ x 384 = 288 CF, plan cross-sectional area = 288 CF ÷ 3.67 ft = 78.47 ft²
  b) Collector blower: LAU #FGP 12-6A
  c) House blower: LAU #FGP 12-6A
  d) DHW COIL: 2 row, 18″ x 24″ (3 ft² size as specified in chart)
  e) Main system ductwork: 8″ x 24″ or the equivalent to 14.6″ (from Table 7.4, rounding up to 400 f²)
  f) Roof collector implies power venting
  g) Required supply register free area: CFM system/100 FPM = 960 CFM/100 FPM = 9.6 ft²
  h) Return air grille and filter; at 300 FPM, face velocity filter size is: 960 CFM ÷ 300 FPM = 3.2 ft² or 461 in.²

TABLE 3.3
CIRCULAR EQUIVALENT OF RECTANGULAR
DUCTS FOR EQUAL FRICTION AND CAPACITY

Dimensions in Inches

Side Rec-tan-gular Duct	4.0	4.5	5.0	5.5	6.0	6.5	7.0	7.5	8.0	9.0	10.0	11.0	12.0	13.0	14.0	15.0	16.0
3.0	3.8	4.0	4.2	4.4	4.6	4.8	4.9	5.1	5.2	5.5	5.7	6.0	6.2	6.4	6.6	6.8	7.0
3.5	4.1	4.3	4.6	4.8	5.0	5.2	5.3	5.5	5.7	6.0	6.3	6.5	6.8	7.0	7.2	7.4	7.6
4.0	4.4	4.6	4.9	5.1	5.3	5.5	5.7	5.9	6.1	6.4	6.8	7.1	7.3	7.6	7.8	8.1	8.3
4.5	4.6	4.9	5.2	5.4	5.6	5.9	6.1	6.3	6.5	6.9	7.2	7.5	7.8	8.1	8.4	8.6	8.9
5.0	4.9	5.2	5.5	5.7	6.0	6.2	6.4	6.7	6.9	7.3	7.6	8.0	8.3	8.6	8.9	9.1	9.4
5.5	5.1	5.4	5.7	6.0	6.3	6.5	6.8	7.0	7.2	7.6	8.0	8.4	8.7	9.0	9.4	9.6	9.8

Side Rec-tan-gular Duct	6	7	8	9	10	11	12	13	14	15	16	17	18	19	20	22	24	26	28	30	Side Rec-tan-gular Duct
6	6.6																				6
7	7.1	7.7																			7
8	7.5	8.2	8.8																		8
9	8.0	8.6	9.3	9.9																	9
10	8.4	9.1	9.8	10.4	10.9																10
11	8.8	9.5	10.2	10.8	11.4	12.0															11
12	9.1	9.9	10.7	11.3	11.9	12.5	13.1														12
13	9.5	10.3	11.1	11.8	12.4	13.0	13.6	14.2													13
14	9.8	10.7	11.5	12.2	12.9	13.5	14.2	14.7	15.3												14
15	10.1	11.0	11.8	12.6	13.3	14.0	14.6	15.3	15.8	16.4											15
16	10.4	11.4	12.2	13.0	13.7	14.4	15.1	15.7	16.3	16.9	17.5										16
17	10.7	11.7	12.5	13.4	14.1	14.9	15.5	16.1	16.8	17.4	18.0	18.6									17
18	11.0	11.9	12.9	13.7	14.5	15.3	16.0	16.6	17.3	17.9	18.5	19.1	19.7								18
19	11.2	12.2	13.2	14.1	14.9	15.6	16.4	17.1	17.8	18.4	19.0	19.6	20.2	20.8							19
20	11.5	12.5	13.5	14.4	15.2	15.9	16.8	17.5	18.2	18.8	19.5	20.1	20.7	21.3	21.9						20
22	12.0	13.1	14.1	15.0	15.9	16.7	17.6	18.3	19.1	19.7	20.4	21.0	21.7	22.3	22.9	24.1					22
24	12.4	13.6	14.6	15.6	16.6	17.5	18.3	19.1	19.8	20.6	21.3	21.9	22.6	23.2	23.9	25.1	26.2				24
26	12.8	14.1	15.2	16.2	17.2	18.1	19.0	19.8	20.6	21.4	22.1	22.8	23.5	24.1	24.8	26.1	27.2	28.4			26
28	13.2	14.5	15.6	16.7	17.7	18.7	19.6	20.5	21.3	22.1	22.9	23.6	24.4	25.0	25.7	27.1	28.2	29.5	30.6		28
30	13.6	14.9	16.1	17.2	18.3	19.3	20.2	21.1	22.0	22.9	23.7	24.4	25.2	25.9	26.7	28.0	29.3	30.5	31.6	32.8	30
32	14.0	15.3	16.5	17.7	18.8	19.8	20.8	21.8	22.7	23.6	24.4	25.2	26.0	26.7	27.5	28.9	30.1	31.4	32.6	33.8	32
34	14.4	15.7	17.0	18.2	19.3	20.4	21.4	22.4	23.3	24.2	25.1	25.9	26.7	27.5	28.3	29.7	31.0	32.3	33.6	34.8	34
36	14.7	16.1	17.4	18.6	19.8	20.9	21.9	23.0	23.9	24.8	25.8	26.6	27.4	28.3	29.0	30.5	32.0	33.0	34.6	35.8	36
38	15.0	16.4	17.8	19.0	20.3	21.4	22.5	23.5	24.5	25.4	26.4	27.3	28.1	29.0	29.8	31.4	32.8	34.2	35.5	36.7	38
40	15.3	16.8	18.2	19.4	20.7	21.9	23.0	24.0	25.1	26.0	27.0	27.9	28.8	29.7	30.5	32.1	33.6	35.1	36.4	37.6	40

SIZING, ENGINEERING,
AND MATERIALS

TABLE 3.3, Continued
CIRCULAR EQUIVALENT OF RECTANGULAR
DUCTS FOR EQUAL FRICTION AND CAPACITY

Side Rec-tan-gular Duct	6	7	8	9	10	11	12	13	14	15	16	17	18	19	20	22	24	26	28	30	Side Rec-tan-gular Duct
42	15.6	17.1	18.5	19.8	21.1	22.3	23.4	24.5	25.6	26.6	27.6	28.5	29.4	30.4	31.2	32.8	34.4	35.9	37.3	38.6	42
44	15.9	17.5	18.9	20.2	21.5	22.7	23.9	25.0	26.1	27.2	28.2	29.1	30.0	31.0	31.9	33.5	35.2	36.7	38.1	39.5	44
46	16.2	17.8	19.2	20.6	21.9	23.2	24.3	25.5	26.7	27.7	28.7	29.7	30.6	31.6	32.5	34.2	35.9	37.4	38.9	40.3	46
48	16.5	18.1	19.6	20.9	22.3	23.6	24.8	26.0	27.2	28.2	29.2	30.2	31.2	32.2	33.1	34.9	36.6	38.2	39.7	41.2	48
50	16.8	18.4	19.9	21.3	22.7	24.0	25.2	26.4	27.6	28.7	29.8	30.8	31.8	32.8	33.7	35.5	37.3	38.9	40.4	42.0	50
52	17.0	18.7	20.2	21.6	23.1	24.4	25.6	26.8	28.1	29.2	30.3	31.4	32.4	33.4	34.3	36.2	38.0	39.6	41.2	42.8	52
54	17.3	19.0	20.5	22.0	23.4	24.8	26.1	27.3	28.5	29.7	30.8	31.9	32.9	33.9	34.9	36.8	38.7	40.3	42.0	43.6	54
56	17.6	19.3	20.9	22.4	25.2	26.5	27.7	28.9	30.1	31.2	32.4	33.4	34.5	35.5	37.4	39.3	41.0	42.7	44.3	56
58	17.8	19.5	21.1	22.7	24.2	25.5	26.9	28.2	29.3	30.5	31.7	32.9	33.9	35.0	36.0	38.0	39.8	41.7	43.4	45.0	58
60	18.1	19.8	21.4	23.0	24.5	25.8	27.3	28.7	29.8	31.0	32.2	33.4	34.5	35.5	36.5	38.6	40.4	42.3	44.0	45.8	60
62	18.3	20.1	21.7	23.3	24.8	26.2	27.6	29.0	30.2	31.4	32.6	33.8	35.0	36.0	37.1	39.2	41.0	42.9	44.7	46.5	62
64	18.6	20.3	22.0	23.6	25.2	26.5	27.9	29.3	30.6	31.8	33.1	34.2	35.5	36.5	37.6	39.7	41.6	43.5	45.4	47.2	64
66	18.8	20.6	22.3	23.9	25.5	26.9	28.3	29.7	31.0	32.2	33.5	34.7	35.9	37.0	38.1	40.2	42.2	44.1	46.0	47.8	66
68	19.0	20.8	22.5	24.2	25.8	27.3	28.7	30.1	31.4	32.6	33.9	35.1	36.3	37.5	38.6	40.7	42.8	44.7	46.6	48.4	68
70	19.2	21.0	22.8	24.5	26.1	27.6	29.1	30.4	31.8	33.1	34.3	35.6	36.8	37.9	39.1	41.3	43.3	45.3	47.2	49.0	70

Reprinted by permission from *1977 ASHRAE Handbook of Fundamentals.*

SYSTEM AIR FLOW RATE. This should be adjusted to remain at 2.5 CFM/SF$_C$ (square foot of collector area) for both the collector loop and house loop air flow rates. For collectors less than 200 ft^2, use 3 CFM/SF$_C$.

ROCK BIN VOLUME. This should be adjusted to remain at ¾ cubic feet of rock per square foot of collector. The plan cross-sectional area of rocks in the bin can be obtained by dividing the volume by 3.67 feet. The height of the rocks in the rock bin should remain constant at 3'8" to give an overall rock bin height of 6'6".

COLLECTOR BLOWER. The blower will remain as called out in Table 3.2. The speed of the blower should be field-adjusted with the adjustable pulleys, in order to reach the desired air flow rate delivery with the existing ductwork. This should be done by a mechanical heating/cooling contractor. The horsepower draw of the blower should also be checked with an amp-probe.

HOUSE BLOWER. Operating conditions will change for this blower, too, as the air flow rate to the house decreases with decreasing collector area. The same comments apply to the house blower as to the collector blower.

DHW COIL. This is reduced in size, as specified in the table; the face area is reduced to maintain a constant air velocity through the coil of approximately 300–350 FPM. The exception to this rule of thumb is a limit on the coil size on the 400–500 SF$_C$ systems to not larger than 18" x 24". In all cases the nearest equivalent standard-size coil should be used since hot water preheating performance is not very sensitive to the coil size.

DUCTWORK. This should be adjusted according to Table 3.1. If other than round or 8 in. sizes are desired, go to Table 3.3 with the round duct size, and read the two rectangular duct dimensions. It is important to adjust the duct size to save costs and facilitate integration of the ductwork into the building space.

SUPPLY REGISTER FREE AREA. This should be adjusted by dividing the system air flow rate in CFM by 100 FPM (the resulting outlet velocity will minimize drafty conditions of supply air temperatures down to 85°F). CFM system/100 FPM = free area (ft²). The free area is not the total grille area, but must be found for each grille in the manufacturer's literature.

Air Supply

The three most significant factors determining what portion of house heating needs will be met with solar in a given climate are the collector size, storage size, and the house insulation level. Another factor of importance is the rate of air delivery to the house from the rock bin or collector. In order to maintain comfortable house temperatures, the energy losses from the house to the ambient have to be replaced by an equivalent amount of energy from the solar system or auxiliary. The important point here is that the rate of heat supply has to equal the rate of heat losses or the house temperature will drop. The rate of heat supply from any hot-air heating system, including solar, depends on the volumetric air flow rate (CFM) and the temperature of the supply air. The energy delivered by a small amount of hot air can be equalled by a larger amount of warm air.

If the rate of air delivery from the solar system to the house, and the rock bed temperature, are both too low to meet the house heat requirement, then the second stage of the thermostat will be activated as the house temperature drops and will in turn engage the backup auxiliary heating system. The energy delivered by the backup system is replacing energy that could perhaps have been supplied by solar; this decreases the solar system utilization and reduces cost-effectiveness. The penalty would be greatest for large solar systems on tight houses, since these solar systems would be capable of meeting the heating requirements of the house most of the time if the air delivery rate to the house were sufficient. Small systems would not be penalized since most of the time there would not be enough energy available to meet the heating load, and auxiliary backup heating would have been required in any case. The point is that, if solar energy is available, it should be used as much as possible to prevent excessive backup heating. The MODEL-TEA control system has this capability, since on a call for heat, the solar-heated air is used whenever it is hot enough to be comfortably supplied to the house without creating cool drafts. If further heating is required, then the auxiliary backup is turned on to augment the solar-heated air.

Supplying too much air to the house creates other problems, such as requiring larger, more costly ductwork, a larger house blower, and, in particular, more and larger supply registers. Increased register space is needed to reduce the drafty feeling resulting from supplying a large amount of relatively cool air to a living area. Warm-air furnaces normally deliver air at 140°F, which permits relatively high velocities at the supply registers. For solar-heated supply air at temperatures as low as 85°F, it is necessary to limit register face velocities to roughly 100–150 FPM, with 100 FPM being preferable. If 1000 CFM were being delivered to the house, sufficient registers would have to be specified to equal 10 SF of free outlet area (1000 CFM/100 FPM = 10 SF).

As a compromise between excessive system costs and system performance, the air supply to the house is chosen here to be such that the same ductwork size used in the rest of the system can be utilized. This is a good compromise, since larger systems will have a large air supply rate to the house, which is needed; and smaller systems will have a small air supply rate to the house, which will not really penalize these systems because less solar energy is available for distribution. The appropriate air supply rates, ductwork size, and register free outlet areas are included in the pre-engineered systems sizing chart in Table 3.1.

BLOWERS. Centrifugal blowers with forward-curved blades are normally used in residential heating and cooling equipment and are applicable to all but the smallest solar systems. If sized properly, they can provide efficient and quiet air movement. Centrifugal blowers with backward-inclined blades are less available and more costly than forward-curved blowers, but generally operate at higher efficiencies over a wider range of conditions. Backward-inclined blowers can be noisier than forward-curved blowers because they operate at higher speeds. An advantage of backward-inclined centrifugal blowers is that they will not overload when system conditions change. For most applications of the MODEL-TEA system, forward-curved blowers will be satisfactory.

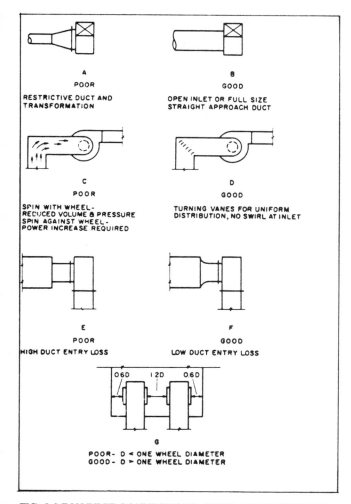

FIG. 3.3 FAN INLET CONNECTIONS. FROM *1979 EQUIPMENT HANDBOOK*, REPRINTED WITH PERMISSION OF ASHRAE.

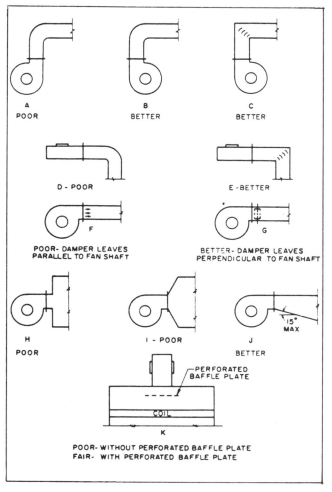

FIG. 3.4 FAN OUTLET CONNECTIONS. FROM *1979 EQUIPMENT HANDBOOK*, REPRINTED WITH PERMISSION OF ASHRAE.

Blowers are sized by specifying the CFM (volumetric air flow) and the system static pressure (usually in units of inches of water column). Careful attention should be given to ensure that the outlet velocity of the air is reasonably low (not above 1700 FPM, preferably between 1000–1600 FPM), and that the blower horsepower requirements are minimized. Often several blowers will be acceptable, but the one that is operating most efficiently will require the least electrical cost to run. To learn more about blowers and duct design consult the *ASHRAE Equipment Volume* (1979), the *ASHRAE Handbook of Fundamentals* (1977), *HVAC Duct System Design* by SMACNA (See Appendix B).

The suggested blowers for the MODEL-TEA air systems are the LAU-FGP series, single inlet, four-way discharge, belt-driven blowers or an equivalent. These blowers are also sold under the Dayton label. If the four-way discharge option is not required, the LAU-BD series performs almost identically. Belt-driven blowers are preferable, since the motor is not situated in the air stream, as is the case with direct drive blowers. With adjustable pulleys, the blowers will accommodate a wide range of operating conditions. Suggested blowers are specified in Table 3.2

Blower outlets should be connected to the system ductwork by gradual transitions (See Figures 3.2 and 3.3 from the ASHRAE *Fundamentals* and *Equipment* volumes), with not greater than a 7° slope of elements for diverging and not greater than 15° slope for converging transitions. Fan inlet and outlet ducts should be as straight as possible. Inlets should have a full-size straight approach duct if possible, and outlet ducts should be straight (or with a gradual transition) for a length of at least 2½ duct diameters. The blower should be connected to the system duct work by unpainted canvas connectors (or other flexible material). See Appendix A. The flexible canvas connector reduces vibration noise.

SYSTEM DUCTWORK. The paramount concern when designing and constructing system ductwork is to eliminate air leakage. Air leakage in some duct systems has been found to be as high as 40% of design flow. Needless to say, this has a devastating effect on performance. Strict industry procedures should be earnestly followed in making all ductwork connections. Leaks in liquid systems are physically destructive, but in air systems they are neither physically damaging nor easily detectable. However, air leakage does have a deleterious effect on the performance of a solar system.

In general, round ducts are easier to leakproof than rectangular ones. SMACNA's *HVAC Duct System Design Manual* recommends that the fiberglass ductwork be in conformance with SMACNA's *Fibrous Glass Duct Manual*, but that the metal duct be sealed in conformance with the Medium Pressure Duct Standards, at the very least. If low-pressure ductwork is used, all joints must be sealed very carefully with a high quality duct tape or its equivalent.

Sizing the ductwork is important; ducts which are too small are noisy (since the air velocity is high) and require excessive blower power to move air through them. Standard rectangular sizes are 8 in. x 4 in. to 8 in. x 30 in. in two inch increments (8 in. x 4 in., 6 in., 8 in., 10. . . . 30 in.). With rectangular duct work it is best to use "short way" angles (45° angle) and elbows (90° angle) with 4 in. radius throats for all bends wherever possible. The pressure drop through these fittings is much less than through the "long way" fittings. Good design practices should be used to avoid excessive pressure drops and leakage in system duct work. Guidelines for duct work sizes are given in the pre-engineered systems sizing chart in Table 3.1.

Domestic Hot Water Option

Schematics are shown in Figures 3.5 and 3.6 for alternative DHW installations. The first uses a specially designed solar tank as the preheat tank. Since this has two additional ports on the side, it enables a simpler plumbing arrangement to be used. The second method uses a conventional tank, similar to the one already employed for the conventional hot water system. This tank only has two ports, inlet and outlet, located at the top. This arrangement necessitates the use of an antisyphon device and a slightly more complex plumbing system. In addition to a tank and the coil, either system requires a pump, valves, and controls.

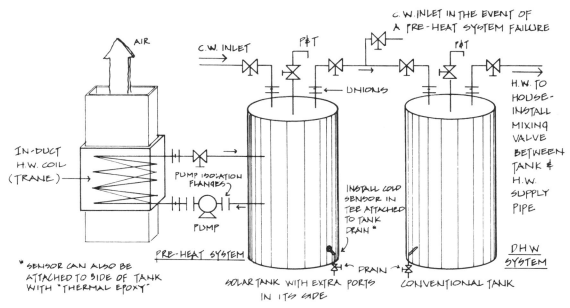

FIG. 3.5 SOLAR-TANK/CONVENTIONAL-TANK DHW SYSTEM

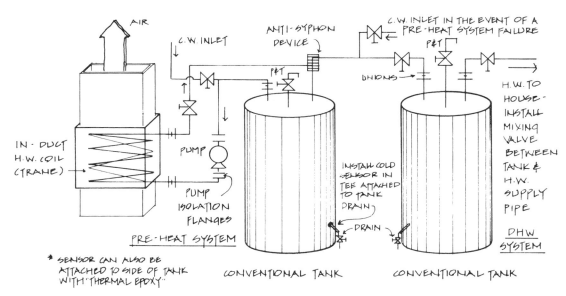

FIG. 3.6 TWO-CONVENTIONAL-TANK DHW SYSTEM

3.4 RECOMMENDED MATERIALS

The review and selection of materials was perhaps the single most critical aspect of the design development. The material requirements of the delivery and storage systems were somewhat familiar, but the collector provided a very challenging set of demands. The materials required for a typical solar collector are the glazing, absorber plate, paint or coating, caulk, insulation, frame, and fastening hardware. In choosing these materials, the most important considerations are usually performance, durability, cost and attractiveness. But for a site-fabricated collector, materials must also be readily available and easy to handle and fabricate. Ideally, a site-built collector should be constructed from standard building materials which are familiar to the builder.

However, a collector is a much more demanding application of materials than normal building construction. The collector materials are subject to extreme temperature variations over a 24-hour period, and large daily temperature differences between the inner and outer layers. They must endure intense ultra-violet radiation and high temperatures for at least twenty years, while still maintaining all their desirable physical properties and retaining the airtight and watertight joints. It is a difficult problem, because on the one hand the materials should be standard, familiar, inexpensive, and commonly available, but on the other hand they must perform outstandingly well in an application which is far more exacting than standard building construction.

The final choices for the MODEL-TEA were the result of an extensive assessment of all materials available for site-built solar systems. Clearly, in order to satisfy conflicting requirements, some compromises had to be made. Standard aluminum industrial siding was chosen for the absorber plate. The only reasonable alternative was galvanized steel siding, but that is not readily available in the configuration required. The aluminum necessitated the use of more expensive fasteners in order to prevent galvanic corrosion, but that was considered to be an acceptable compromise. The exact configuration of the siding was determined by theoretically optimizing the collector performance. Thermo-ply™, a foil-faced impregnated fiber sheathing, was selected to be placed over the studs or rafters, forming the back side of the air channels. The Thermo-ply provides an airtight surface and prevents the wood from being directly exposed to the hot air blown through the collector. It also has the benefit of reducing the collector's thermal capacitance by helping to thermally separate the collector from the mass of wood in the rafters or studs. The foil face of the Thermo-ply, together with the unpainted back of the aluminum absorber, greatly reduces heat transfer from the absorber to the sheathing. This results in a slight decrease in instantaneous collector efficiency, but that was calculated and found to be offset by the increase in daily performance due to the lower thermal capacitance.

The ends of the absorber are closed with EPDM rubber end closure strips which are purchased with the absorber. There are different types of EPDM closure strips and these differ in their tolerance of high temperatures. Pure (100%) EPDM closure strips will endure normal collector operating temperatures (140°F) with no significant degradation, and can tolerate temperatures up to 250°F, although such high temperatures should never occur. Some closure strips are referred to as "EPDM" even though they are really a blend of EPDM, neoprene, and SBR (styrene-butadiene rubber). These should definitely be avoided, as they will deteriorate at lower temperatures (150–200°F). Closure strips composed of other materials, such as PVC (polyvinylchloride), should also be avoided as they will soften at low temperatures. Thus the only type of closure strip recommended is 100% EPDM.

Caulking materials are essential to obtaining airtight joints, and it is critically important that the manifold pans and absorber make a leak-free envelope. Two types of high-performance caulk are recommended for the MODEL-TEA. Silicone caulk is a high performance material capable of withstanding temperatures up to 400°F without serious degradation. However, its skin-over time is too short (less than ten minutes) to allow its use in normal sandwich or layered joints in site-built construction. Silicone can only be used to seal corner-type joints, after the pieces have been fastened together. Urethane caulk is the recommended material for the standard layered joints on the collector. Its tack-free and skin-over times are sufficiently long to allow proper caulking and positioning of large sheets of collector materials. The adhesive properties are excellent, and it can tolerate temperatures up to at least 275°F without degradation.

The absorber requires a flat black surface which has long-term durability under extreme temperature variations. Both paints and selective coatings were evaluated, and although selective coatings improve collector efficiency, they were not chosen due to their higher cost and incompatibility with the site-built approach. Epoxy-base paints have often been used in collectors because the paint cures by chemical reaction, minimizing outgassing. However, these paints are very expensive and are not really necessary unless the construction schedule does not allow several days for drying. T.E.A. believes that standard enamel paints, which dry by solvent evaporation, will not cause outgassing problems if they are allowed to dry completely (at least two full days). The recommended paint for the absorber is any standard oil-base flat black enamel of proven durability and sufficient temperature tolerance.

Vertical battens are placed over the absorber plate to support the glazing. Good, straight, dry wood should be used for these, either spruce or fir, but definitely *not* pine. Pine outgasses at low temperatures and the resin will coat the glazing, reducing transmittance. Aluminum can be used for the battens, probably providing longer term durability, but at a significant extra cost. The details of the aluminum batten option are given in Chapter 8.

Steel screws cannot be used to fasten the battens to the aluminum absorber, as galvanic corrosion will result. The recommended fasteners are stainless steel or aluminum.

The recommended glazing material is single glass for the roof collector and double glass for the wall. T.E.A. conducted computer simulations of collector performance and cost for double vs. single glazing and found that, if collector area is optimized according to life cycle economics, single glazing is competitive with double in all parts of the country. A slightly larger collector with single glazing will deliver roughly the same energy at the same cost as a smaller collector with double glazing. In other words, the increased efficiency (in most areas of the country) of double glazing is roughly offset by the extra cost. Thus, on the roof, where there is usually more area than needed, a large single-glazed collector can be constructed, with the added advantage that single glass is much easier to handle on a roof than double glass. But on a wall application, area is usually very limited, so double glazing is used to collect the most energy per

square foot. Handling double glass in vertical wall applications
is not as difficult as it would be on a roof.

Glass was chosen as the best glazing material after a thorough evaluation of all available materials. Its durability and
visual aesthetics are unsurpassed. High-transmittance solar
glass can be purchased with either an ordinary flat surface or a
textured surface which reduces reflections and glare. T.E.A.
tested acrylic, fiberglass-reinforced polyester, and thin film
glazings in the hope that one such lower cost material would
be acceptable. None were. (See Appendix A for more detailed
information.)

The glazing system chosen to fasten the glass to the collector
consists of strips of EPDM rubber and an aluminum bar as the
outer batten. The glass is held between two strips of EPDM, the
inner one being fastened to the wood batten. The outer aluminum batten is screwed to the absorber through the EPDM and
the inner batten. This glazing system is very easy to install, and
requires almost no caulking material. T.E.A. thoroughly investigated other methods of fastening the glazing, and actually
tested three other glazing systems. A wood batten and caulk
system was tested on collector modules. On a roof mock-up, a
standard greenhouse system and an extruded EPDM system
were tested. More detailed information on these decisions and
on specific materials and sources is contained in Appendix A.

3.5 PURCHASING MATERIALS

A discussion of materials and sources of supply is given in
Appendix A. All materials must be on hand before beginning
construction, and certain materials may require special ordering
and significant waiting periods.

SHEET METAL COLLECTOR MANIFOLDS. The sheet metal manifolds
must be ordered from a sheet metal shop, and formed to exact
specifications. They should be ordered as early as possible
since there may be significant delays, and the first work on the
collector involves the manifolds.

CAULK. Urethane caulk is readily available at hardware stores and can also be ordered directly from manufacturers. GE Silicone caulk is available at many building-supply stores. Caulk is required at the beginning of construction, and there should always be a sufficient quantity at the site so that it can be used liberally.

THERMO-PLY SHEATHING. If possible, Super-Grade Blue Thermo-ply should be used, rather than Structural-Grade Red. Unfortunately, the "Structural" is more widely available. Many building supply stores carry it, and any that do can order the "Super." The problem is that they must order a minimum of 200 sheets and they may not have enough demand to justify that. If this difficulty does occur, it is possible to contact the manufacturer directly (see Appendix A) to locate the nearest source. A lead time of six of eight weeks may be necessary.

ALUMINUM SIDING. The aluminum siding can be ordered from a number of distributors across the country. The EPDM end closures should be ordered with the siding and must be ordered to fit the "inside" of the selected rib pattern. It is *important* to note that the 4-inch rib pattern is not completely symmetrical: the flat valleys which are against the Thermo-ply are narrower than the flat raised sections. The *only* recommended rubber end closure strips are those made of 100% EPDM. A minimum lead time of six to eight weeks may be necessary.

PAINT. If a standard flat black paint is used (such as Rustoleum #412), there will be no problem with availability. If an epoxy or selective paint is chosen, it will have to be ordered directly from the manufacturer, along with the appropriate primer and reducer.

PAINT SPRAYER. A paint sprayer and a protective face mask will be needed for painting the absorber. The painting should be done on a dry, windless, dustless day, and the paint should be allowed to dry thoroughly before it is sealed over by the next layer of the collector. The absorber should be clean and dry when the glazing is installed; all surfaces should be as dust-free as possible.

GLASS. Low-iron glass may be available from local glass distributors. The name of the nearest distributor can be obtained from the manufacturer. Four to six weeks should be allowed for delivery. Single glass is used on the roof collector, and double-glazed panels on the wall collector. The double-glazed panels must have a flexible seal between the panes, to allow for independent expansion and contraction of each sheet. Double-glazed units with a glass-fused or metal edge should not be used. They will break under extreme differential temperatures.

CRUSHED ROCK. The ¾ in. to 1½ in. rock should be readily available. It is important that the rock be clean, so it should be washed twice. If the rock supplier will not wash the rock a second time, the builder will have to wash the rock on site. Since that is a difficult undertaking, every effort should be made to have the supplier do all the washing. The rock should be thoroughly dry before it is loaded into the storage bin.

SPECIAL SHEET METAL WORK. Custom sheet metal work may be required not only for the collector manifolds, but also for transitions to the blowers. If this is the case, a local sheet metal shop should be contacted to do the work, and there might be delays of up to two weeks. The slide dampers and backdraft dampers should either be constructed by the builder or fabricated by a sheet metal shop.

AIR-HANDLING AND CONTROL EQUIPMENT. Most of the air-handling equipment is available through local heating contractors, or from local distributors. Some equipment, such as blowers, can also be ordered from a catalog supply house (e.g., W.W. Grainger).

CHAPTER 4

CONSTRUCTING THE ROOF COLLECTOR

The MODEL-TEA roof collector has several advantages over the wall collector: it doesn't interfere with lighting or views from living spaces, because it usually occupies an unused space; more collector area can be constructed, because the available space is usually larger on a roof than on a wall (there will be fewer shading problems in the winter on a roof); combined with direct gain passive solar heating on the south wall, a higher solar heating fraction can be reached. A domestic hot water system can be built into the air-handling system, resulting in energy gains year round and a shorter payback period.

The instructions on how to build the MODEL-TEA roof collector are meant for persons familiar with wood frame construction — skilled contractors, carpenters, or owner-builders. The key word is skill: the ability to perform the tasks, based on working knowledge gained from carpentry experience. The more experience, the easier these instructions will be to follow.

This chapter, plus Chapter 6 on constructing the rock bin (if there will be remote storage) and Chapter 7 on the MODEL-TEA System Control Wiring, should be read thoroughly before beginning to order materials, and before beginning any stages of construction.

The experienced carpenter will have most of the tools necessary to build this collector, but may have to borrow or rent a few specialized ones. Among the tools needed are:

hammer, screwdrivers, tapes, pliers, tin snips, chalk line, caulking gun, staple gun, handsaws, circular saw, table saw, sabre saw (optional), soldering iron (optional), paint sprayer, power screwdriver or variable speed/reversible drill

The MODEL-TEA roof collector can be built into new construction, or retrofitted into existing buildings. The instructions are for new construction, with *additional* special instructions for retrofit where applicable.

RETROFIT: These sections *must* be read by those who are retrofitting the MODEL-TEA, and can be skipped for new construction.

Before installing the collector on the roof, certain calculations must be done and decisions must be reached. First, the system

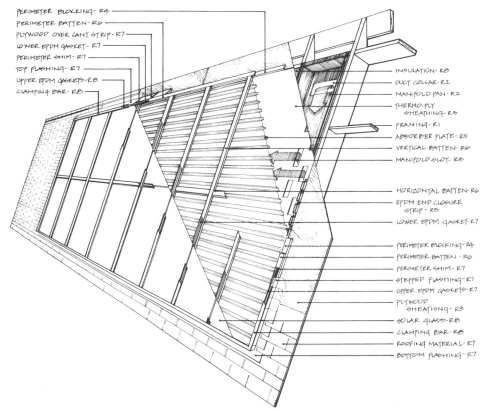

PERIMETER BLOCKING- R4
PERIMETER BATTEN- R6
PLYWOOD OVER CANT STRIP- R7
LOWER EPDM GASKET- R7
PERIMETER SHIM- R7
TOP FLASHING- R7
UPPER EPDM GASKETS- R8
CLAMPING BAR- R8

INSULATION- R8
DUCT COLLAR- R2
MANIFOLD PAN- R2
THERMO-PLY
SHEATHING- R3
FRAMING- R1
ABSORBER PLATE- R5
VERTICAL BATTEN- R6
MANIFOLD SLOT- R3

HORIZONTAL BATTEN- R6
EPDM END CLOSURE
STRIP- R5
LOWER EPDM GASKET- R7

PERIMETER BLOCKING- R4
PERIMETER BATTEN- R6
PERIMETER SHIM- R7
STEPPED FLASHING- R7
UPPER EPDM GASKETS- R7
PLYWOOD
SHEATHING- R3
SOLAR GLASS- R8
CLAMPING BAR- R8
ROOFING MATERIAL- R7
BOTTOM FLASHING- R7

FIG. 4.1 MODEL-TEA ROOF COLLECTOR

must be sized according to the heating load of the building. This should be done using the rules in Section 3.1, resulting in a square foot area for the collector.

4.1 COLLECTOR SIZING

Second, the size of the glass must be selected to fit the square foot size of the collector, and to fit on the roof. The glass comes in two standard widths (34 in. and 46 in.) and two standard heights (76 in. and 96 in.). In conjunction with the CY/RO Universal Glazing System, you must allow 1 in. between each sheet of glass, plus an additional 3¼ in. for the sides (or top and bottom, not including the cant strip), plus the width or height of the glass itself. Use the following formulas to calculate the width and height of the collector:

Collector width in inches = (glass width in inches x no. of panels) + (1 in. x no. of panels) + 2½ in.

Collector height in inches = (glass height in inches x no. of panels) + (1 in. x no. of panels) + 2½ in.

If the collector were to be glazed with eight panels of 34-in.-wide glass, side by side, the collector width would be: (34 x 8) + (1 x 8) + 2½ = 282½" or 23'6½".

If the collector were to be glazed with two panels of 96-in.-high glass, the collector height would be: (96 x 2) + (1 x 2) + 2½ = 196½" or 16'4½".

Compare the calculated width with the width of the roof. A minimum distance should be left between each side of the collector and the edge of the roof, to allow for the intersection of the side wall and roof. Then compare the calculated height with the height of the roof. Allow approximately 9 in. above the collector for the cant strip and flashing. The lowest the collector can extend to the bottom of the roof is where the south wall intersects the roof.

Third, determine the number of manifold pans that will be needed, and their size. In an average collector (about 24 feet wide), there are two manifold pans built into the roof. One will supply cool air to the collector, and one will take the hot air away. The manifold pan which is closest to the remote storage or living space to be heated will be the return pan. The shorter the duct run, the less the heat loss. It is next to this pan that the temperature sensors will be located.

The maximum distance between the outsides of the supply and return manifold pans should be 26 feet. If the collector is wider than this, additional manifold pans must be introduced at the centerline of the collector. The two manifold pans at the sides of the collector will be the supply pans, and the two at the center of the collector will be the return pans. In this case, it is next to one of the *center* pans that the temperature sensors will be located.

**TABLE 4.1
ROOF COLLECTOR SIZES**

COLLECTOR WIDTH

No. of Panels	34" Glass	46" Glass
2	6'0½"	8'0½"
3	8'11½"	11'11½"
4	11'10½"	15'10½"
5	14'9½"	19'9½"
6	17'8½"	23'8½"
7	20'7½"	27'7½"
8	23'6½"	31'6½"
9	26'5½"	35'5½"
10	29'4½"*	39'4½"†

COLLECTOR HEIGHT‡

No. of Panels	76" Glass	96" Glass
1	6'7½"	8'3½"
2	13'0½"	16'4½"
3	19'5½"§	24'5½"″

* For larger collectors, add 35" per panel.

† For larger collectors, add 47" per panel.

‡ Not including cant strip

§ For larger collectors, add 77" per panel.

″ For larger collectors, add 97" per panel.

Holes for the duct collars, connecting the supply and return ducts to the manifold pans, must be located in the manifold pans. If there are only two pans, the return duct collar hole is placed in the top or bottom corner of the pan (whichever is closest to storage), and the supply duct collar to the other pan in the opposite corner. For example, if the return duct is in the lower left of the collector, then the supply duct will be in the upper right (see detail 1 on roof drawing 2). However, if there are four manifold pans, this changes slightly. The two return manifold pans are in the center of the collector. The two supply manifold pans are on the outside of the collector. If the return ducts are attached to the center manifolds at the top of the collector (they both must be side by side since they feed into the same return duct), then the supply ducts are attached at the two bottom outside corners. If the return ducts are in the bottom center, then the supply ducts are at the top outside.

Wherever the return duct is located, the temperature sensors will be located next to the manifold where it is attached.

The size of the manifold pans depends on the area of the collector. Section 3.1 discusses how to size the manifold pans. Remember that the collector area used in the calculations to size the pans is the area located between pairs of manifold pans. If there is one supply and one manifold pan, the area used in the calculations is the full area of the collector. If there are two supply pans and two return pans, then the area used in the calculations will be half the actual area of the collector.

The dimensions arrived at in Section 3.1 will be the inside dimensions of the pans. Allow for the thickness of the pan material itself when determining the actual "manifold pan width" used so often later.

Fourth, decide whether the system will have remote storage or not, and if it will have a domestic hot water (DHW) preheating system. If the collector is connected directly to the living space, without using remote storage, it is called a "daytime system." These systems will have a relatively small collector area (less than 200 square feet), and the domestic hot water preheating mode would probably not be included because it wouldn't be cost effective.

If the system does have the DHW mode, there will be five temperature sensors connected to the collector. One is for the normal winter operation of the collector. The second is for the summer power venting operation, the third and fourth are for the overheating alarms, and the fifth is for the DHW mode. If there is no DHW mode, the last one can be eliminated. These sensors will be located near the return duct collar connection to the return manifold pan.

It is very important to remember during construction that, unless the pieces are assembled very carefully, the glass panels will not fit into the spaces allotted for them. There is a ¼-in. gap (shown on the drawings and called for in the instructions) around each pane of glass. This gap is *vital* to allow glass to

expand. If it is not there, the glass will crack. Therefore, be
absolutely sure that all the dimensions are correct, and that all
the blocking is square. Check and double check each dimension carefully.

Go through the drawings step by step with the instructions,
until everything is clear. The drawings are not meant to be
used without the instructions, nor are the instructions meant to
be used without the drawings. Make notes on the drawings of
those things that depend on site conditions. Write in the actual
dimensions you determine and calculate how much of each material needs to be ordered; order through the manufacturers
found in Appendix A.2, in the sequence described in Section
3.5. Read through materials descriptions in Appendix A.1; such
things as which type of caulk to use with which joint are discussed there.

The step by step instructions in this and succeeding chapters
are keyed to the construction drawings on the foldouts, found
elsewhere in the book. Each construction step has a key number, and a corresponding key sketch in the margin where the
step begins. Each construction step has a corresponding drawing, which you will find on the appropriate foldout.

As you read each section, you will be asked to refer to details
on the construction drawings. For example, you might see
(3-R6) at the end of a sentence. This would mean "refer to detail
3, on roof collector drawing number 6." Turn to roof collector
drawing number 6, and you will see a 6 in the upper right hand
corner with the word "ROOF" below it. The key sketch is there,
as well as the title of the page and the step: *Battens*. As you
refer back and forth from instructions to drawings, look for these
four things: the drawing number, the word ROOF, the key
sketch, and the title of the page. It is important that the instructions and the drawings are used together.

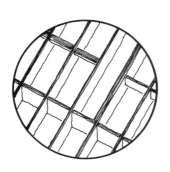

4.2 FRAMING

The framing of the roof serves as the base of the MODEL-TEA
roof collector (1-R1). The outer manifold rafters mark where the
sides of the collector will be attached, and the top and bottom
blocking mark the upper and lower collector limits. It is impor-

tant that the rafters be parallel, and that the horizontal runs of
blocking be parallel with each other and perpendicular to the
rafters.

The manifold bays will house the manifold pan (1,2-R1), so
be sure they are a little wider than the outside manifold pan
dimension.

Rafters

Frame the roof with 2 x (nominal) rafters spaced at 24 in. on
center (1-R1). The depth of the rafters will depend on their actual span/design load. The collector itself will increase the dead
load on the rafters by approximately 7 psf (pounds per square
foot). It is assumed in the drawings that the centerline of one
rafter will lie along the centerline of the roof. If a rafter is not
centered on the roof, it only means that the collector will not be
centered on the roof. This will not affect collector performance.
It is essential, however, that the centerline of one rafter (the
"center-rafter") lie along the centerline of the collector.

The outermost rafters under the side edges of the collector are
the *outer manifold rafters* (1-R1). To locate these two rafters,
divide the total width of the collector in half, subtract ¾ in. and
measure out this distance to each side of the centerline of the
centerrafter. Frame the centerlines of the two outer manifold
rafters at these two points.

The rafters framed just inside the outer manifold rafters will be
the *inner manifold rafters*. Add 3 in. to the manifold pan width
(determined in Section 3.1) and measure in this distance from
each outer manifold rafter. Frame the centerlines of the inner
manifold rafters here. The space between the outer and inner
manifold rafters is the *manifold bay*.

If the manifold bay (pan) width plus 1½ in. is greater than 24
in. on center, double both the inner and outer manifold rafters.
Frame one rafter to the inside of the outer manifold rafter, and
one to the side of the inner manifold rafter *outside* the manifold
bay. If the collector width is great enough to warrant inner
manifold pans (greater than 26 ft.), frame these manifold bays to
each side of the center rafter, in the same way the outer manifold bays were framed. If this manifold bay width is greater

FIG. 4.2 BUILDING FRAMING FOR THE COLLECTOR

than 24 in. on center, triple the center rafter, and double the outer manifold rafters *outside* the manifold bays.

When fastening the collar ties, fasten them to the outside of the rafters at the manifold bays (not inside the manifold bays) so they won't interfere with the manifold pans.

RETROFIT: Important! If there are any electrical wires in the roof, turn off the electric power at its source. Remove the shingles in the general area where the collector will be. Lay out the perimeter lines of the collector on the sheathing, checking the diagonals between corners to make sure the lines are square.

RETROFIT (continued): The width and height will be the full collector width and height. Snap the lines with a chalk line. Remove the sheathing inside these lines. Mark the center line of the collector on the sheathing at a point 4 in. above and below the perimeter lines.

Examine the rafters. Their depth and spacing must structurally be able to carry an additional 7 psf of dead load. Books on wood frame construction have tables listing how much live and dead load a rafter can hold, given certain sizes and spacings. If there are any doubts, consult a structural engineer.

Frame new rafters with their centerlines vertically along the edges where the sheathing was removed.

From the sides of the collector, measure in the width of the manifold pan, plus 3¾ in. Frame the centerline of the inner manifold rafters here, forming the manifold bays. If this distance is greater than the on-center spacing of the rafters, double up on the new rafters outside the manifold bays.

If the collector is greater than 26 feet wide, frame new rafters to form two manifold bays at the centerline of the collector. If the bays are greater than the on-center spacing of the rafters, triple up on the center rafter, and double up on the manifold rafters to each side of it. Frame the extra double-up on the manifold rafters to each side of it. Frame the extra rafters outside the manifold bay, so that the manifold pan will fit in the bay.

Remove any blocking insulation or electrical wires in the manifold bays. Reframe collar ties outside the manifold bays. Cut 1½-in. strips of ½-in. plywood, and fasten down the sides of the collector, with their inside edges along the centerline of the manifold blocking.

Collector Blocking

Lay out the collector height on one of the rafters. Check the highest and lowest points with a piece of blocking the depth of the rafters, to be sure the ridge pole, soffit or south wall will not interfere with the collector. If it does, shift the collector height up or down on the roof. If there is still interference, a new glazing height for the collector will have to be found. Return to the introduction and refigure. Mark the centerline of the collector on the rafter. Divide the collector height in half, subtract 2 in. and mark this distance above and below the centerline. Fasten the centerline of the 2 x (nominal) collector blocking at these points. The depth of the blocking should equal the depth of the rafters. The blocking will be in a continuous straight line from one outer manifold rafter to the other. Since the blocking joints will not be staggered, toe-nail the blocking at one end. Make sure that the top 1½ in. face of the blocking is flush with the top of the rafters (3-R1).

RETROFIT: Fasten the 2 x (nominal) collector blocking horizontally across the top and bottom of the roof opening, with the centerline along the edge where the sheathing was removed.

Manifold Blocking

Fasten 2 x 4 (nominal) blocking to the inside of the outer manifold rafters, and to both sides of the center rafter (if there are to be inner manifolds). This blocking is parallel to, and flush with, the top of the rafters (2-R1). It is continuous from the top to the bottom collector blocking.

If the manifold rafters were doubled up because the width of the manifold pans was greater than 24 inches, the extra rafter *is* the manifold blocking, and will be called the "manifold blocking" (2-R1).

Sheathing Blocking

Measuring down from the centerline of the top collector blocking, fasten 2 x 4 (nominal) horizontal blocking across the roof at 4'0" on center (1-R1). This blocking is continuous across the roof, with its 3½ in. face flush with the face of the rafters (3-R1). Do not stagger this blocking, but toe-nail at one end. *Do not* install this blocking in the manifold bays, because it would interfere with the manifold pans. *Do* install it outside the manifold bays, with its 1½ in. face flush with the face of the rafters, including it along the same centerline as the collector blocking.

If the collector is greater than two glass panels high, frame the lower half of the collector with 2 x 6 (nominal) sheathing blocking, rather than 2 x 4. Install the 2 x 6 with its 5½ in. face flush with the face of the rafter. The blocking outside the collector area may remain 2 x 4s, with their 1½ in. faces flush with the rafters.

RETROFIT: Follow the new construction instructions, but eliminate the blocking outside the collector area. Since the roof is already sheathed, it is not necessary.

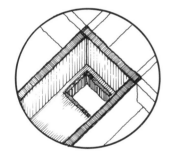

4.3 MANIFOLD PANS

The purpose of the manifold pans is to distribute air the full height of the collector. The supply and return ducts are connected to the manifold pans. The air from the supply duct flows through the duct collar (3-R2) and fills the manifold pan, supplying the air to the full height of the collector. At the return manifold side, the hot air from behind the absorber plate will first fill the return manifold pan, then will be drawn away by the duct collar at the bottom of the pan. The duct collars must be connected to the manifold pans with an airtight seal, or leakage will occur and performance will be lost.

Prefabricate the manifold pans and duct collar inserts to the dimensions determined in Section 3.1: the interior dimensions of the pan. Have them made of 30-gauge galvanized sheet metal, with 1½ in. nailing flanges. Horizontal corners must overlap vertical corners. Solder all joints and all overlaps (2-R2).

Arrange the duct openings in the manifold pans according to instructions earlier in this chapter. The duct openings should have the same cross-sectional area as the manifold pan (its width times its depth).

There are two ways to fasten the duct collar inserts to the manifold pans. One is to drop the inserts into the pans and solder. The other is to lay a ¼-in. continuous bead of urethane

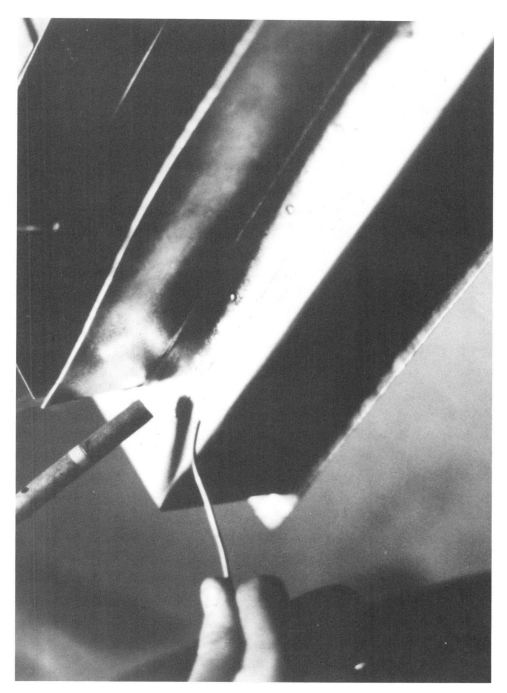

FIG. 4.3 SOLDERING THE DUCT COLLAR TO THE MANIFOLD PAN

caulk around the duct connection openings inside the manifold pans, and drop the duct collar inserts into the openings (2, 3-R2). Fasten with #6 x ¼ in. Phillips pan head sheet metal screws at 6 in. on center. Drop the manifold pans into place in the manifold bays, with the nailing flanges over the supports. Fasten the pans with 1 in. galvanized roofing nails at 6 in. on center around the nailing flanges. (See Appendix A for urethane caulk recommendations.)

RETROFIT: If the room behind the collector is finished, the piece of rigid fiberglass insulation that will fit behind the manifold pan must be placed in the manifold bay before the pan is (2-R8). Cut the piece just big enough that it will fit snugly in the bay. Wedge it into the bottom of the bay, and then drop the manifold pan in on top of it.

4.4 SHEATHING

The air from the supply manifold pan flows through the slots cut in the collector sheathing (1-R3). The air flows across the face of the collector, between the sheathing and the absorber plate. Therefore, the seams in the sheathing must be airtight to keep the air from leaking through the back of the collector. For the same reason, the edge of the collector sheathing and the roof sheathing must be airtight. This is accomplished with caulk, but also with support from rafters and horizontal blocking. Caulk is also applied around the nailing flanges of the manifold pans so that air cannot leak between the pans and the sheathing.

Thermo-Ply Collector Sheathing

Thermo-ply Super Strength (blue) sheathing (an ⅛-in. foil-faced structural/insulative sheathing) is shown as the collector sheathing on the drawings.

It is important that the four edges of the sheathing be supported by either blocking or the rafters, horizontally *and* vertically. This is for structural reasons and to minimize air leakage between the sheets of sheathing and the back of the collector.

Beginning at the centerline of the collector, lay sheathing horizontally across the collector, running a continuous bead of urethane caulk along the edge of one before butting to the edge of the next. Cut the perimeter sheets to fit (1-R3).

Fasten the Thermo-ply with 1-in. galvanized roofing nails or $7/_{16}$-in. crown divergent staples at 4 in. on center around the panel edges, and 8 in. on center at the intermediate supports. Cover the entire collector from the centerline of one outer manifold blocking to the other, and from the centerline of the top to the centerline of the bottom collector blocking.

Apply a ¼-in. continuous bead of urethane caulk around the inside edge of the nailing flanges of the manifold pans just before laying a sheet of Thermo-ply over them (1-R3). It is *vital* to not apply this caulk until you are ready to lay a sheet of sheathing over it. The caulk will skim over quickly, especially on hot sunny days, and must be replaced if it hardens before the sheathing goes on.

If the collector has center manifolds, snap a chalk line down the centerline of the collector on the face of the Thermo-ply.

Plywood Roof Sheathing

Finish sheathing the rest of the roof with ½-in. CDX plywood. Run a ¼-in. continuous bead of caulk along the edge of the Thermo-ply before butting a sheet of plywood against it (3, 4-R3). Fasten the plywood with 8d common nails at 6 in. on center around the panel edges and 1 '0" on center at intermediate supports.

Mark the centerline of the collector on the plywood, at a point 4 in. above and below the Thermo-ply perimeter. These marks will be very important as reference points.

Manifold Slots

Slots are cut in the Thermo-ply to allow the air to pass out of the manifold pans and behind the absorber plate ribs. They are cut in the following pattern so that every rib in the absorber plate will be fed air from the manifold pan. Snap a chalk line 3 in. to the inside of the edge of the plywood sheathing at the sides of

---

the collector, parallel to the rafter and extending the full height of the collector. Snap three more lines, parallel to the first, and spaced 3 in. apart, toward the inside of the collector. Repeat the process at the other outer manifold rafter (1, 2-R3). If there are center manifold pans, repeat this process to each side of the collector centerline.

Beginning at the edge of the top sheet of Thermo-ply, mark the following lines between the chalk lines *closest* to the side edge of the Thermo-ply (or centerline of the collector): 2½ in., 9 in., 8 in., 9 in., 8 in., 9 in., 2½ in. Repeat this process down each sheet of

FIG. 4.4 CUTTING THE MANIFOLD SLOTS

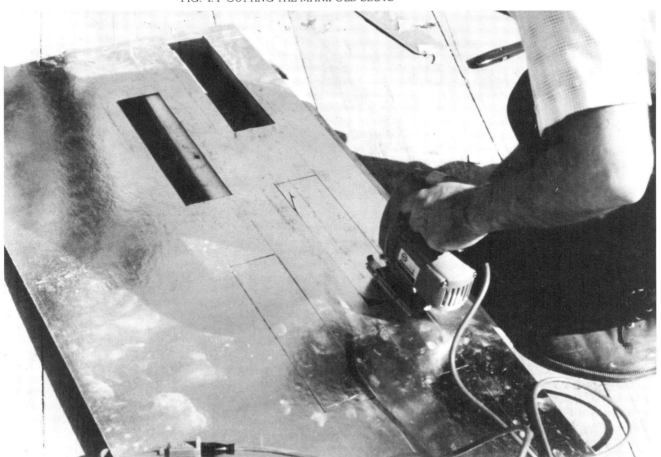

Thermo-ply between all the pairs of chalk lines *closest* to the side of the collector. If the bottom sheet is an irregular size, end the last hole a minimum of 2½ in. above the bottom seam (1, 2-R3).

Between the pairs of chalk lines *furthest* from the sides (or the centerline of the collector) mark the following lines perpendicular to the chalk lines: 11 in., 9 in., 8 in., 9 in., 11 in. Repeat this process down each sheet of Thermo-ply between all the pairs of chalk lines *furthest* from the rafters. Again, if the bottom sheet is an irregular size, end the last hole a minimum of 2½ in. above the bottom seam (1, 2-R3).

With a sabre saw or utility knife, carefully cut out all rectangles that measure 9 in. x 3 in. The only rectangles of different dimensions that should be cut would be the lowest rectangles on the collector, ending 2½ in. away from the bottom edge of the Thermo-ply. Remove all pieces of Thermo-ply from manifold pans.

Drill one ⅛-in.-diameter hole in the Thermo-ply for every temperature sensor to be used, near the return manifold duct connection. These holes will be lined up with the absorber plate ribs, beginning with the bottom rib, one hole per rib (1-R3). They should be located horizontally at a distance in from the side of the collector (or from the centerline of the collector centerline if the return manifolds are in the center of the collector) equal to the manifold pan plus 4 inches. These holes are for the wires attached to the temperature sensors that will be connected to the Thermo-ply.

Temperature Sensors

There are a maximum of five temperature sensors that will be located near the return manifold pan. The first two are mandatory: one is for winter operation of the collector, and the other is for summer power venting. The third sensor, which operates the domestic hot water mode, should be mounted only if there is to be a DHW preheating system. The fourth and fifth sensors, for overheating protection, are mandatory. Attach each one to the Thermo-ply, located next to the holes drilled for the sensor wires (1-R3). Each sensor should be fastened according to its manufacturer's instructions. Attach wires to the sensors if they are not

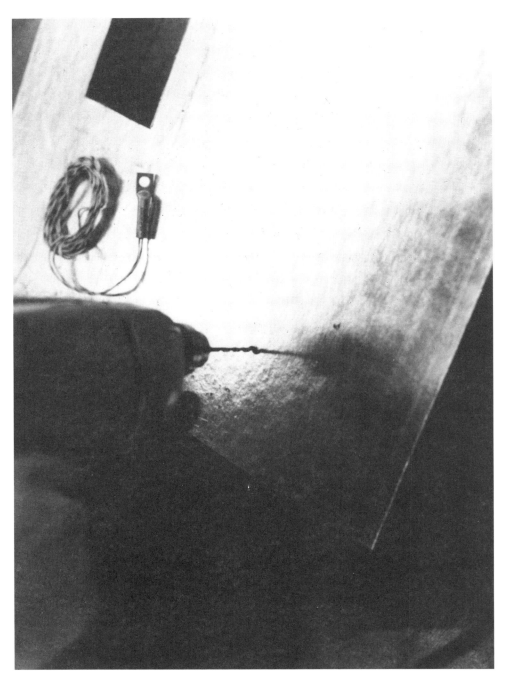

FIG. 4.5 DRILLING A HOLE FOR TEMPERATURE SENSOR WIRE

already attached. Check the manufacturer's specifications for the type of wire, because some sensors require shielded wire. Fasten the top edge of the absorber plate sheet to the roof. Tie a knot in each wire, and position it over its respective ⅛-in-diameter hole in the Thermo-ply (3-R5). This will keep the wires from being pulled out of the sensors, after the wires are fed through the holes. Feed the wires through each hole, and then caulk the holes in the Thermo-ply. Write with a felt marker on the back side of the Thermo-ply which sensor is which (e.g., "T_C " for normal winter collector operation, "T_{COL} " for summer venting, "T_{CHW} " for DHW control, T_{HL1} and T_{HL2} for overheating protection).

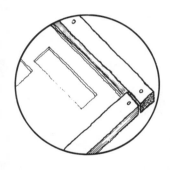

4.5 PERIMETER BLOCKING

The perimeter blocking not only sets the boundaries for the absorber plate to be fastened within, but is also the beginning of the framework for the glazing. It is vital that these pieces be square with each other, and be fastened to the exact dimensions required. Therefore, follow the sequence of laying out and checking diagonals carefully. Check the dimensions several times to be sure they are correct. Any miscalculation *now* could mean the glass won't fit later.

Cut 1 x (nominal) #2 select fir or spruce (do not use pine; it is not a suitable wood to use anywhere between the collector sheathing and the glazing) planks into 2¼-in. and 2-in. widths. Tack the 2-in. width across the top and bottom of the collector, with the ¾-in. face flush with the edge of the plywood (3-R4). Tack the 2¼ in. width down the sides of the collector, with the ¾-in. face flush with the edge of the plywood (2-R4). Maintain the straightness of the blocking over long distances. Check the diagonals from the outside corners of the blocking. Adjust the blocking until the diagonals are equal (within ¼ in. of each other). If the blocking is not square, each step from here on will magnify the error, with the result that the glass will not fit.

When the blocking is square, fasten it with 3 in. drywall screws at 1'0" on center.

4.6 ABSORBER PLATE

The air from the supply manifold pan passes through the manifold slots in the Thermo-ply into the ribs of the absorber plate. It flows between the back surface of the absorber plate's ribs and the face of the Thermo-ply, carrying away the heat from the surfaces as it passes by. It is then pulled through the slots into the return manifold pan. The absorber plate is painted black to absorb more of the sun's light, and reflect less back to the outside.

It is very important that every edge of the absorber plate, including the overlaps, be airtight. Leakage through the absorber plate can mean the difference between a good collector and a poor one. Therefore, be generous with the urethane caulk. And don't skimp on the screws. The number called for will help keep the aluminum expansion to a minimum. The less the plate moves, the longer the seal of the caulk will hold.

The absorber plate is made of 8-in. ribbed aluminum industrial siding sheets (49¾ in. actual width, 48 in. coverage, .032-in.-thick aluminum with the mill finish). (See Appendix A for manufacturer recommendations.) Note that the siding will be applied to the roof with the 1⅜-in. rib valley fastened flush with the Thermo-ply. The 5⅝-in. rib will be one inch above the Thermo-ply (3-R5).

Enough sheets will be needed to cover the face of the Thermo-ply (1-R5). Use the following two equations to determine the number of sheets to order, and their lengths:

No. of sheets (round off to next highest whole number) =
(collector height in inches − 4 in.)/48 inches
Sheet length (round off to next highest 6 in.) = (collector width in inches − 4½ in.)

For example, if the collector were the same one used as an example in the introduction to this chapter (23′6½″ wide × 16′4½″ high), the number of sheets ordered would be: (16′4½″ − 4 in.)/4 ft. = four sheets. The actual sheet length would be: (23′4½″) − (5 in.) = 23′0½″. But the sheets must be ordered in 6 in. increments, so they would be 23 ft. 6 in.-long sheet sheets.

FIG. 4.6 TACKING THE PERIMETER BLOCKING

The sheets only come in standard lengths up to 30 feet, in increments of 6 inches. If the collector is longer than 26 feet, and has inner manifolds, divide the collector width in half and use two sheets to cover the width. The sheets will *butt* together at the centerline of the collector, between the two inner manifold pans.

At the ends of each sheet there will be a high temperature, pure EPDM end closure strip. Order enough "inside" end closure strips by the linear foot to close off all ends of the sheets. For example, if the collector is one sheet wide, order two times the height of the collector. If it is two sheets wide, order four times the height. There will be two sets of EPDM end closure strips at the centerline of the collector, between the two inner manifolds.

The sheets will probably have to be cut both horizontally and vertically. Horizontal and vertical cuts can be made using a hand-held circular saw (with a carbide blade). Cuts across the rib can also be made with a pair of tin snips. Cuts along the rib or rib valley can be scored with a utility knife, and the siding is then bent back and forth until the metal breaks clean. When using the circular saw, wear eye and ear protection and a respiration mask while cutting. Cutting the sheet may raise or bend the edge slightly. Remove the raised areas with a file or utility knife, and straighten the edge with a pair of pliers.

Cut the sheets to the width required to fit horizontally across the collector (e.g., 23'0½"). Save a 49⅝-in.-long piece of ribbed scrap, cut from the end of the sheet, to be used later. Cut ⅝ in. horizontally from the top of the rib valley of the top sheet (3-R5), leaving ¾ in. left as the valley width. The bottom sheet will be cut after all the other sheets are in place on the roof and an actual measurement can be taken.

Sheet Preparation

To remove the thin film of oil that will be found on the sheets and prepare them for painting, sponge down the outside of the sheets with a solution of trisodium-phosphate (TSP) powder dissolved in water. Rinse the sheets with water. Next, etch the

FIG. 4.7 SIDING AND EPDM END CLOSURE STRIPS

FIG. 4.8 CUTTING AN ABSORBER PLATE SHEET ALONG THE RIB

sheets with muriatic acid according to manufacturer's instructions. The TSP powder and muriatic acid are both available at
hardware or building supply stores.

Using the scrap piece of siding as a guide, and a ¼-in. continuous bead of urethane caulk as the adhesive, lay out and
stick the end closure strips for the *first* sheet of ribbed siding to
the roof (2-R5). The caulk must still be "wet" to act like a glue, so
don't let it skim over before pushing the closure strips into it. Fit
the ribs of the closure strip into the ribs in the scrap piece.
Following the form of the siding will keep the closure strip from
becoming stretched out as it is stuck in the caulk. Begin at the

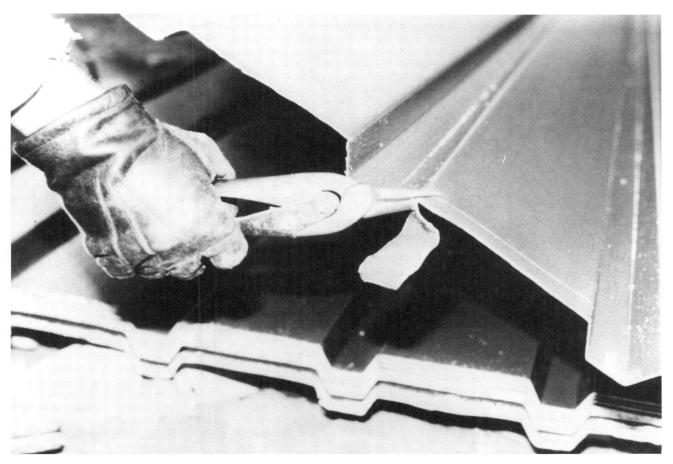

FIG. 4.9 CUTTING AN ABSORBER PLATE SHEET ACROSS THE RIB

top perimeter seam between the Thermo-ply and the plywood, and line the strips up with the side seams between the two sheathings.

If the collector has center manifolds, run one strip down each side of the collector centerline snapped in the Thermo-ply (see Figure 4.10). *Do not* let the caulk skim over before covering it with the siding. If it does, remove it and caulk again.

Just before the first sheet is ready to be taken up to the roof, run a ¼-in. continuous bead of caulk over the inside top edge of the EPDM end closure strips. Run the same size continuous bead along the top perimeter seam of the collector. Butt the top

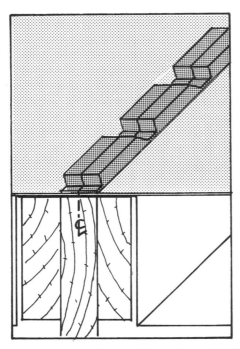

FIG. 4.10 CENTERLINE EPDM END CLOSURE STRIPS

edge of the first sheet against the edge of the plywood at the perimeter, laying the sheet carefully over the end closure strips (3-R5). Make sure the end closure strips fit snugly into the ribs.

Fasten the sheet across the top edge with #12 x 1¼ in. Phillips pan head aluminum or 18-8 stainless steel sheet metal screws at 6 in. on center. Fasten vertically through every rib valley at the ends of the sheet, and through every other rib valley at every rafter. *Do not* fasten through the air channels. The rafters can be found by noticing where the nails or staples are in the Thermo-ply. *Do not* fasten across the bottom of the sheet yet.

Lay out and caulk the EPDM end closure strips for the next sheet. Apply extra caulk where these strips butt against those already on the roof. Run a ¼-in. continuous bead of caulk across the top edge of the overlap strip (3-R5). Lift the bottom of the first sheet, and place the top rib valley of the second sheet below it. Position the second sheet over the end closure strips. Lower the first sheet onto the second. Wipe off any caulk that

FIG. 4.11 CAULKING THE SHEET OVERLAP

FIG. 4.12 CAULKING THE EPDM END CLOSURE STRIP

has been forced out, before it skims over. Follow the same fastening schedule as on the first sheet (3-R5). Continue this process for all sheets except the bottom one.

After the next-to-last sheet is on, measure from the top edge of the last rib valley to the bottom perimeter seam between the Thermo-ply and the plywood (3-R5). This distance, plus a ½-in. allowance for the overlap strip, will be the width to cut the last sheet. If the bottom of the last sheet is cut across a rib valley, follow the layout of the end closure strips and the same fastening schedule as the other sheets. Run a ¼-in. continuous bead of caulk along the bottom edge of the Thermo-ply. Lay the ribbed siding over it and fasten at 6 in. on center (3-R5).

If the bottom edge of the last sheet is cut across a rib, follow the layout of the end closure strips and the same fastening schedule as the last sheets. Cut a continuous piece of 1 × 1 in. fir or spruce blocking. Run a ¼-in. continuous bead of caulk along the bottom edge of the Thermo-ply. Lay the continuous blocking in the caulk, and butt its length against the side of the plywood edge, and against the end closure strips at its end. Caulk again along the top edge of the blocking and lay the edge of the last sheet over it. Fasten with #12 x 2½ in. Phillips pan head aluminum or 18-8 stainless steel sheet metal screws at 6 in. on center (see 3-R5). Check the four corners of the collector. The end closure strips may raise the ends of the top and bottom edges slightly, which will cause leaks. If necessary, loosen the screws, add more caulk, then tighten and add more screws.

Priming and Painting

Prime and paint the absorber plate according to the paint manufacturer's instructions. (See Appendix A for recommendations.) Paint the inside surface of any wood exposed around the perimeter of the plate with one coat of each. Allow the paint to dry completely, a minimum of two full days. Standard enamel paints dry by solvent evaporation, a process which should be allowed to finish before the glazing goes on. If there is not enough time to allow for this, an epoxy paint must be used. Once the absorber plate is painted, be careful not to scratch it. Precautions should be taken, such as wrapping ladder legs with rags. Touch up any scratches with paint before the glazing is installed.

FIG. 4.13 BATTEN STRIPS IN POSITION

4.7 BATTENS

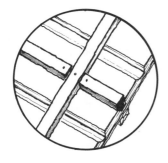

The battens are those vertical members to which the glazing system is attached, so they must be securely fastened to the absorber plate or the perimeter blocking. They must be parallel with each other, and square with those to which they run perpendicular, or the glass will not fit. Check each dimension and diagonal carefully. Then check them again.

Cut 1 x 3 (nominal) fir or spruce (not pine) battens (1-R6). Paint with two coats of flat black paint. Tack the battens around the perimeter of the collector first, making sure the outside edge is flush with the outside edge of the perimeter blocking. Check the diagonals before fastening with 3-in. drywall screws at 1'0" on center (1-R6).

Cut a piece of plywood with a horizontal dimension equal to the glazing width minus 1½ in. and a vertical dimension equal to the glazing height minus 1½ in. This is used as a guide to make sure the battens will be the correct distance from each other. Be sure the sides are square, and the dimensions are exact, especially at the corners.

Fasten the first vertical batten down the centerline of the collector. Check the diagonal to be sure it is square with the perimeter battens. Lay out the battens to each side, fastening down each batten as the plywood guide is run down between it and the preceding one that is already fastened. Fasten with #14 x 1½-in. aluminum or 18-8 stainless steel Phillips flat head wood screws into every other rib. By the time the last one is laid out, the plywood guide should fit between this batten and the preceding one, and between itself and the one fastened to the perimeter blocking (2-R6).

The horizontal battens should be laid out the same way, spaced vertically with the plywood guide. If the horizontal battens fall across a rib, 1 x 3 (nominal) fir or spruce is fastened with #14 x 1½-in. aluminum or 18-8 stainless steel Phillips flat head wood screws at 1'0" on center, with a minimum of three screws per batten. A 1 x 3 (nominal) fir or spruce batten on top of 1 x 2 (nominal) fir or spruce batten is used if the batten falls over a rib valley (3-R6). In this case, fasten with #14 x 3-in. aluminum or 18-8 stainless steel Phillips flat head wood screws at 1'0" on center, with a minimum of three screws per batten.

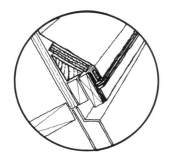

4.8 GLAZING PREPARATION

Preparing the collector for the glazing process consists of several important steps. The first is preparing the bed on which the glazing will lie. It is an EPDM extrusion stapled to all the battens, and will cushion the glass against live loads of wind and snow.

The second step is weatherproofing the perimeter of the collector with flashing. This will keep water from leaking in through the edges of the collector. The canted (sloped) blocking across the top of the collector will allow for good drainage.

The last step, the smoke test, is vital to the performance of the collector. The collector must be thoroughly checked for leaks. As will be seen on the first test, no matter how well the collector was caulked, there will still be spots that were missed. But don't get discouraged—the leaks are not difficult to seal. More than one test, however, will surely be needed to find and seal them all.

The glass will rest on EPDM lower gaskets, one part of the Universal Glazing System (U.G.S.) by CY/RO Industries. Order enough linear feet of the 4-piece system as you have linear feet of battens. (See Appendix A.) The lower gasket has two parallel ridges running up its center.

Glazing Bed

INTERIOR GASKETS. Center the gasket on each of the vertical interior battens (not the perimeter battens), cutting each the length from inside edge to inside edge of the perimeter battens, plus ¼ in. Do not splice sections of the gasket together. Staple the battens with ⁷/₁₆-in. crown divergent staples at 3′0″ on center extending the ends ⅛ in. over the perimeter battens (1, 2-R7). Center the gasket on each of the horizontal interior battens (not the perimeter battens), cutting each the length from vertical gasket to vertical gasket. Staple with ⁷/₁₆-in. crown divergent staples, with a minimum of three per gasket (1, 3-R7).

CANT STRIP. Using 2 x 4s (nominal), cut continuous cant strips the length of the collector. The angle of the cut along the 3½-in. side will equal the angle of the roof pitch minus ten degrees. For example, if the roof slope is 60°, cut the cant strip at 50°. Tack the cant strip above the collector with its 1½-in. side flush with the perimeter of the collector, and its 3½-in. side against the plywood (3-R7). Measure from the upper perimeter batten, vertically across the cant strip, to the plywood on the roof. Cut continuous strips of ½-in. CDX plywood this width, and fasten it continuously across the cant strip with 10d common nails at 1′0″ on center.

PERIMETER GASKETS AND SHIMS. Cut enough $^3/_{16}$ in. x ¾ in. (actual) wood shims to equal the distance around the outside perimeter edge of the perimeter battens. Lay the lower gasket around the perimeter battens, lining up the exterior edge with the exterior edge of the batten. Miter the gasket at the four corners of the collectors. *Do not* splice pieces together on any length, but cut continuous pieces. Lay each of the lengths along the edges, with its corresponding shim lined up with the same edge. Staple through both with $^7/_{16}$-in. crown divergent staples at 3′0″ on center (1, 2, 3-R7). Caulk at all the intersections between horizontal and vertical battens, and at all four mitered corners.

Roofing/Flashing

Roof with chosen material across the bottom of the collector. Bend 10-in.-wide 0.019 in. aluminum flashing over the shim, so the flashing edge is flush with the inside edge of the shim (2-R7), down the side of the batten/blocking and onto the roof, continuously from side to side of the collector. Fasten to the batten, and to the roof, with 1-in. glavanized roofing nails at 1′0″ on center. Cut and bend the flashing around the side corners of the collector. Begin roofing up the sides of the collector, stepping sheets of the same thickness flashing between the roofing. Bend the flashing over, fastening it to the batten and roof in the same manner used across the bottom of the collector. Bend the flashing up and over the cant strip when the top corners are reached, and fasten to the cant strip top and sides. Flash across the cant strip, over the shim across the top of the collector, and fasten with 1-in. galvanized roofing nails at 1′0″ on center. Bend over the sides at the corners of the collector and fasten. Complete the roofing across the roof above the collector (1, 2, 3-R7).

Smoke Test

Before installing the glazing, it is necessary to check for leaks in the system. This is important, since even small leaks reduce the efficiency of the collector dramatically. One method of checking for leaks is a smoke test. This can be done using a metal can and a smoke bomb. (See Appendix A for smoke bomb recommendations.) *Follow manufacturer's warnings.*

It is helpful at this point to have the supply and return ducts attached to the manifold pans, to also check for leaks at the connections.

Seal off the duct connection to one manifold or duct using polyethylene film (or cardboard) and duct tape. Leave the other manifold or duct temporarily open to insert the can.

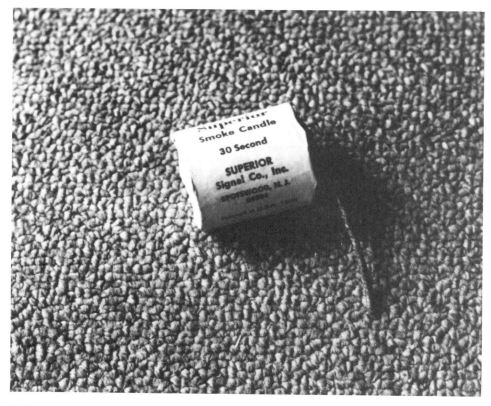

FIG. 4.14 A SMOKE BOMB

FIG. 4.15 SMOKE TESTING THE COLLECTOR
BEFORE THE GLAZING IS INSTALLED

Place the smoke bomb in a paint or soft drink can, ignite it and place it up into the duct or slightly into the manifold. Seal the opening. Carefully check the collector for leaks, and seal all leaks with caulk.

It will not be unusual for the collector to leak slightly around the edges of the absorber plate and at the overlaps, and these leaks must be completely sealed. Adding clear silicone caulk and more screws at these seams will help stop these leaks. Paint over the new screws and any scratches on the plate.

Also check the back of the collector for leaks at the manifolds, ducts, or those made by any fasteners that punctured the Thermo-ply. Caulk all leaks with silicone.

Several tests may be required before all the leaks are sealed. This is an important step in the construction process, so conduct it carefully.

4.9 GLAZING AND FINISHING

The panes of glass allow the sun's light to pass through and hit the absorber plate, but slow the transfer of the resulting heat back to the outside. The glass must be able to expand and contract freely with extreme temperature changes; therefore, the ¼-in. gap allowed around each pane of glass is vital to the survival of the glass.

The aluminum clamping bars with built-in gaskets provide support, along with an *almost* caulk-free weatherproof seal. The only place caulk is needed is at the intersections of the clamping bars, where water could leak in under the bars and, through freezing and thawing, shorten the life of the lower EPDM gaskets.

Glazing

The rest of the glazing process requires mounting sheets of ³/₁₆-in.-thick glass to the collector, using the remaining parts of the CY/RO U.G.S. system. (See Appendix A for glass recommendations.) The last pieces of the U.G.S. system are the aluminum clamping bar and the two upper EPDM gaskets.

Lay out the clamping bars and cut to the same lengths as the lower gaskets were cut (Section 4.8). Miter the corners of the clamping bars at the four corners of the collector battens. The long horizontal sides may have to be done in sections, since the clamping bars come in stock 25-ft. lengths. Try to keep the splices to a minimum. Pre-drill the clamping bars at 8 in. on center along the centerline of the bars, with holes no more than ½ in. from the ends of the bars. Feed the upper gaskets into the channels extruded into the underside of the bars. Run the gaskets *continuously through* any splices of the clamping bars.

Center the clamping bar over the lower gasket, horizontally across the bottom of the collector. Fasten with #12 x 2 aluminum or 18-8 stainless steel Phillips pan head sheet metal screws, with neoprene washers. Fasten all the screws partway in, leaving enough room between the bar and the gasket to fit the glass. Repeat this process up *one* side of the collector.

Before each pane of glass is placed on the collector, place two ¼ x ¼ x 4-in. neoprene (80-90 Shore-A-Durometer) setting blocks at the two quarter-points of each bay. These will keep each pane of glass from sliding down, and are available from local glazing dealers.

Starting at this *same* corner of the collector, center the first pane of glass within the boundaries set by the two clamping bars and the ribs on the lower neoprene gasket. Re-center the lower gaskets on the battens if they were moved as the glass was centered. Tighten the screws on the two clamping bars already in place. Center the other vertical clamping bar over the side lower gasket, and partially fasten the screws, to a point 16 in. below the top of the piece of glass in place. Partially fasten the horizontal clamping bar above the glass. Place the two setting blocks, center the next pane of glass above the first, and reposition the lower gaskets on the battens if they were moved. Tighten the screws across the horizontal clamping bar and the vertical clamping bar at the perimeter. Continue partially fastening the other *side* clamping bar to the *top* of this piece of glass.

Repeat this process until the top of the collector is reached. Do not fasten the horizontal top clamping bar at this time. Caulk between any intersections of the fully fastened clamping bars, including the splices. This caulk will keep water from leaking through the intersections and under the glazing bars.

Return to the bottom of the collector, and continue the glazing from bottom to top of the side of the set just completed. Once a clamping bar has glass on two sides of it, fasten the screws all the way into the wood. Once an intersection is completed, caulk it.

Repeat this process across the collector until the last vertical clamping bar is fastened up the opposite side. Fasten the horizontal top bar, and caulk all remaining intersections.

Interior Finishing

Cut rigid fiberglass insulation the width and length necessary to fit behind the manifold pans, from manifold rafter to manifold rafter and from top to bottom collector blocking. Make the insulation as thick as will fit without protruding beyond the rafters. Locate the sensor wires that were fed through the Thermo-ply. Attach each sensor wire to its respective control and attach each control near the back of the collector (on the back of a rafter or on a nearby wall). Future access to the sensors (by cutting through the back of the Thermo-ply, replacing sensor, and duct-taping the cutout in place again) may be necessary, as well as access to the controls. Attach more wire (shielded wire if manu-facturer's specifications call for it) and run to the air-handling control panel (See Figures 7.19 and 7.20, or 7.26, 7.27, and 7.29). It is important to tag the wires so that they don't become confused with each other. Insulate with fiberglass batt between the rafters behind the collector, the full depth of the rafters. If the space behind the collectors is unheated, insulate to a point at least 6 in. beyond the perimeter of the collector. If the space behind the collector is heated, insulate from east to west wall. Staple a 6-mil polyethylene vapor barrier to the rafters, over-lapping the sheets and taping the edges together. Finish the interior surfaces as desired.

CHAPTER 5

CONSTRUCTING THE WALL COLLECTOR

111

A wall collector has several advantages over a roof collector. First, since it is close to the ground, it is accessible and is easier to build. Second, during the heating season the vertical collector can gain from sunlight reflected from snow on the ground (or light-colored gravel if there is no snow). The double-glazed system means better performance than a single-glazed system, so the collector square footage can be smaller, yet gather the same amount of heat. Third, since the summer sun is higher than the winter sun, much of the sunlight will be reflected off the glazing (rather than passing through it), resulting in lower stagnation temperatures. This means the power venting mode can be eliminated, saving money not only in installation costs, but also in the annual operating costs.

The instructions on how to build the MODEL-TEA wall collector are meant for those persons familiar with wood frame construction: skilled contractors, carpenters, or owner-builders. The key word is skill, the ability to perform the tasks, based on working knowledge gained from carpentry experience.

This chapter, plus Chapter 6, Constructing the Rock Bin (if there will be remote storage), and Chapter 7 on the MODEL-TEA System Control Wiring, should all be read thoroughly before beginning to order materials, and before beginning any stages of construction.

The experienced carpenter will have most of the tools necessary to build this collector, but may have to borrow or rent a few of the special ones. Among the tools needed are:

hammer, screwdriver, tapes, pliers, tin snips, plumb bob, levels, chalk line, caulking gun, staple gun, hand saws, circular saw, table saw, sabre saw (optional), soldering iron (optional), paint sprayer, router, power screwdriver or variable speed/reversible drill

The MODEL-TEA can be built into new construction or retrofitted into existing buildings. The instructions are written for new construction, with additional special instructions for retrofit where needed:

RETROFIT: The instructions for retrofit begin with the word *Retrofit*, and *must* be read by those who are retrofitting the

MODEL-TEA; these sections may be skipped by those building into new construction.

The collector will either be connected to remote storage, or be connected directly to a living space. The drawings and instructions assume that ducts will connect to the bottom of the manifold pans (see wall drawing no. 2, detail 4); the ducts run to remote storage or to a living space. The duct "collars" penetrate the floor and connect to the manifold pans located in the wall cavities at either end of the collector. This floor could be the first floor, with the ducts running into the basement where the remote storage is located. Or this floor could be the second floor of a two-story house, with the ducts running above the first floor ceiling, connecting the collector to the living space. Another option is for the collector to be on the wall of the first floor, but connect the duct collars to the tops of the manifold pans. Again, the ducts could be run in the second floor. If the wall the collector is built into sits on a slab, the duct collars can either enter at the top of the manifold pans, or enter through the back of the pans. In the latter case, the ducts will intrude upon the living space, and will have to be boxed in and finished to match the space. These ducts can either run across the floor, or across or into the ceiling.

There are many variations which can be made, depending on the site, the location in relation to living spaces, framing, or even personal taste. When making any change, think it through, and mark changes on the drawings before beginning the construction process.

5.1 COLLECTOR SIZING

Before installing the collector, certain calculations must be done and decisions must be reached. First, the system must be sized according to the percentage of the heating load it is to provide. This should be done using the rules in Section 3.1, resulting in a square foot area for the collector.

Second, the size of the glazing must be selected to fit the square foot size of the collector, and to fit on the wall. The glass comes in two standard widths (in inches): 34 and 46, and two standard heights: 76 and 96. In conjunction with the CY/RO Universal Glazing System, you must allow 1 in. between each sheet of glass, plus an additional 3¼ in. for the sides (or top and bottom, not including the cant strip or the sill), plus the width or height of the glass itself. Use the following formulas to calculate the width and height of the collector:

Collector width in inches = (glass width in inches x no. of panels) + (1 in. x no. of panels) + 2½ in.

Collector height in inches = (glass panel height in inches) + 9 in.

For example if the collector were to be glazed with four panels of 46-in.-wide glass side by side, the collector would be:

(46 x 4) + (1 x 4) + 2½ = 190½" or 15' 10½" wide.

If the collector were to be glazed vertically with one panel of 96-in.-high glass, the collector would be:

(96 x 1) + 9 = 105" or 8'-9".

Although it is possible to build a two-story collector, the drawings show a one-story-high collector. We recommend building the two levels as separately manifolded units, or inserting a duct connection (much like the duct collar detail described in Section 5.3 and on wall drawing number 2) between the floors as shown in Figure 5.1. Support is needed across the bottom of each pane of glass, and that support must have setting blocks and weep holes (see Fig. 5.1).

Compare the calculated width to the width of the space the collector is to fit into. A minimum distance should be left between the side of the collector and the end of the wall to allow for the intersection of the east or west wall with the south wall. Allow approximately 9 inches above the collector for the cant set and flashing.

Third, determine the number and size of manifold pans that will be needed. In an average width collector (about 24 feet

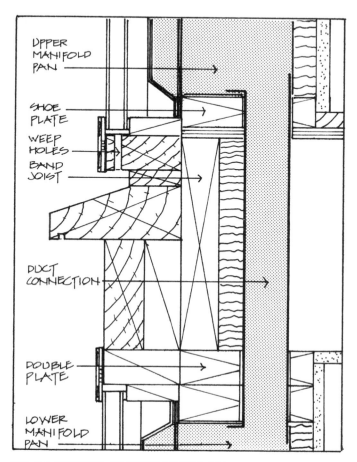

UPPER MANIFOLD PAN

SHOE PLATE

WEEP HOLES

BAND JOIST

DUCT CONNECTION

DOUBLE PLATE

LOWER MANIFOLD PAN

FIG. 5.1 VERTICAL SECTION OF TWO-STORY WALL
COLLECTOR AT INTERSECTION WITH FLOOR

wide) there are two manifold pans built into the wall: one to
supply cool air to the collector, and one to take the hot air
away. The manifold pan which is closest to the remote storage,
or living area to be heated, will be the return pan. The shorter
the duct run, the less the heat loss. It is next to this pan that the
temperature sensors (discussed below) will be located. The
maximum distance between the outsides of the supply and return manifold pans should be 26 feet. If the collector is longer
than this, additional manifold pans must be introduced at the
centerline of the collector. The two manifold pans at the sides of

TABLE 5.1
WALL COLLECTOR SIZES

COLLECTOR WIDTH

No. of Panels	34″ Glass	46″ Glass
2	6′0½″	8′0½″
3	8′11½″	11′11½″
4	11′10½″	15′10½″
5	14′9½″	19′9½″
6	17′8½″	23′8½″
7	20′7½″	27′7½″
8	23′6½″	31′6½″
9	26′5½″	35′5½″
10	29′4½″*	39′4½″†

COLLECTOR HEIGHT‡

No. of Panels	76″ Glass	96″ Glass
1	7′1″	8′9″
2	min. 14′3¾″	min. 17′7¾″
3	min. 21′6¼″	min. 26′6½″

* For larger collectors, add 35″ per panel.

† For larger collectors, add 47″ per panel.

‡Height is from bottom of sill to top of cant. Minimum height for collectors greater than one panel high: assume 11¼″ between glass panels.

the collector would be the supply pans, and the two at the center of the collector will be the return pans. In this case, the temperature sensors would be located next to one of the center pans.

The size of the manifold pans depends on the area of the collector. Section 3.1 discusses how to size the manifold pans. Two things must be remembered when sizing the pans for a wall collector. One, the actual depth of the pan in a 2 x 6 stud wall will be 4½ in., and in a 2 x 4 wall it will be 2½ in. This dimension allows for the 1-in.-thick insulation that is located between the back of the manifold pans and the interior face of the studs. The second thing to remember is that the area of the collector used in the calculations is the area between manifold pans. If there is one supply and one return manifold pan, the area used in the calculations is the full area of the collector. If there are two supply pans and two return pans, then the area used in the calculations will be half the actual area of the collector. The dimensions arrived at in Section 3.1 will be the inside dimensions of the pans. Allow for the thickness of the pan material itself when determining the actual "manifold pan width" used so often later on.

Fourth, determine the width of the rib on the industrial siding used as the absorber plate (see Section 5.6). If the collector is less than 16 feet wide, the 4-in. rib should be used. If the collector is equal to or greater than 16 feet, the rib should be 8 in. The 4-in. rib comes in sheets that are 45⅝ in. wide, with an "actual coverage" of 44 in. (the sheets are overlapped). The 8-in. rib comes in sheets that are 49⅝ in. wide, with an "actual coverage" of 48 in.

Fifth, decide whether the system will have remote storage or not, and if it will have a domestic hot water (DHW) preheating system. If the collector is connected directly to the living space without using remote storage, it is called a "Daytime System." These systems will have a relatively small collector area (less than 200 square feet), and the domestic hot water preheating mode will probably not be included, because it wouldn't be cost effective. This means that only *two* temperature sensors will be connected in the collector. If there is a domestic hot water preheating system, there will be *three* sensors connected to the plate. These sensors will be located near the return manifold.

It is very important to remember that, unless the pieces are put together very carefully, the glass panels will not fit into the spaces allotted for them. There is a ¼-in. gap (shown on the drawings and called for in the instructions) around each panel of glass. This is vital to allow space for the glass to expand. If it is not allotted, the glass will crack. Therefore, be absolutely sure that all dimensions are correct, and that all blocking is square. The constant use of a plumb bob and line level is highly recommended. Check at the end of each step that the materials installed in that step are square and level.

Go through the drawings step by step with the instructions, until everything is clear. The drawings are not meant to be used without the instructions, nor are the instructions meant to be used without the drawings. Make notes on the drawings of those things that are changed due to site conditions. Write in the actual dimensions you calculated. Determine how much of each material needs to be ordered, and order through the manufacturers found in Appendix A.2; see the sequence described in Section 3.5. Read the materials descriptions in Appendix A.1; such things as which type of caulk should be used with which type of joint are discussed there.

The following step-by-step instructions are keyed to the construction drawings on the foldouts found elsewhere in this book. Each construction step has a key number, and a corresponding key sketch in the margin where the step begins. Each construction foldout has the same key sketch in the upper righthand drawing.

As you read each section, you will be referred to details on the construction drawings. For example, you might see (3-W6) at the end of a sentence. This would mean, refer to detail 3, on wall collector drawing number 6. Turn to wall collector drawing number 6, and you will see a number 6 in the upper righthand corner with the word "Wall" below it. The key sketch is there, as well as the title of the page and the step: Battens. As you refer back and forth from instructions to drawings look for these four things: the drawing number, the word Wall, the key sketch and the title of the page. It is important that the instructions and the drawings are used together.

5.2 FRAMING

The framing doubles as a wall of the house and as the foundation of the MODEL-TEA collector (1-W1). The outer-manifold studs mark where the sides of the collector will be attached, and the horizontal blocking marks where the top and bottom will be attached. It is important that the studs be plumb (use a plumb bob to check) and the horizontal blocking be level (use a level) for the collector perimeters to start out square.

The manifold bays will house the manifold pans (2, 3-W1), so be sure they are a little wider than the outside manifold pan dimension. The insulation between the headers over the pan will help reduce heat loss directly through the wood (3-R1). The slot cut through the shoe plate and the subfloor is for the duct collar insert that will be attached to the pan. The insulation below it will help reduce heat loss from the duct collar to the outside.

Studs

Lay out the 2 x 6 (nominal) wall plates (top and shoe) side by side, and mark across both where the centerline of the center stud will be. The two outermost studs under the side edges of the collector will be the *outside collector studs*. To locate these two studs, divide the total width of the collector in half, subtract 1¼ in. and measure out this distance to each side of the centerline of the center stud. Mark the centerlines of the two outer collector studs at these points. Mark the centerline of one stud, which will be flush inside each of the collector studs. These will be the *outer manifold studs* (2-W1). (The distance from centerline to centerline of the studs is the same as the distance from outside edge to outside edge, or inside edge to inside edge.)

The next studs to the inside of these will be the *inner manifold studs*. Add 3 in. to the outside manifold pan width, determined in Section 3.1, and measure in the distance from the centerlines of the outer manifold studs. Mark the centerlines of the inner manifolds studs here. The space between the outer and inner manifold studs is the *manifold bay*. This space must be as wide, or wider, than the outer dimension of the manifold pan (not including the nailing flanges).

If the manifold bay (pan) width plus 1½ in. is greater than 24 in. on center, double the inner manifold stud, *outside* the manifold bay. These manifold bays will have to be framed with headers, whose sizes depend on the width of the bay. Use Table 5.2 to determine the size header needed (1, 3-W1).

If the collector width is great enough to warrant inner manifold pans (greater than 26 ft), mark manifold bays to each side of the center stud, as described above. If the manifold bay

TABLE 5.2
HEADER SIZES FOR LOADS AND SPANS

SIZE	LOAD/SPAN		
two headers on edge	two floors and roof	one floor and roof	roof only
2 x 4	2 ft	3 ft	4 ft
2 x 6	4 ft	5 ft	6 ft

width is greater than 24 in. on center, triple the center stud, and double the outer manifold studs outside the manifold bays.

Lay out the glazing studs from the centerline of the collector, at a distance on center equal to the glazing width plus 1 inch. Mark the centerline on the plates. Fill in with studs between the glazing studs, so that no distance will be greater than 24 in. on center, except in the manifold bays (1-W1).

Frame the 2 x 6 (nominal) studs between the two plates, on the centerlines marked with 10d common nails. Fasten the headers (with 2½ in. of rigid insulation and blocking in between them) over the manifold studs (3-W1). Tip the wall into place, brace and plumb.

> **RETROFIT:** Important! Turn off the electricity to the south wall. Remove the siding in the general area where the collector is to be. Lay out the perimeter lines of the collector on the sheathing, using a line level and a plumb bob. Check the diagonals to be sure the lines are square. The width and height will be the full collector width and height.
>
> Snap chalk lines at the collector perimeter. Set a circular saw to the depth of the sheathing, and cut along the chalk lines. Remove the sheathing inside the collector area. Frame studs and horizontal blocking *behind* the plywood, with their edges flush with the edges of the plywood. Frame the outer collector studs, manifold studs, and glazing studs as outlined above. Install let-in bracing (if it doesn't already exist) across the face of the studs, *except* in the manifold bays.

Blocking

The location of the collector vertically on the wall depends on the height of the glazing being used and the sill-to-header height of the wall. Looking at (3-W5), and the relationship between the top and bottom of the absorber plate to the manifold pan, the collector can move up or down on the wall. But the top and bottom rib of the absorber plate *must* be overlapped at least 5 in. for 8-in. rib, (1 in. for 4-in. rib), over the manifold pans. If either full rib width is above or below the manifold pan, air will not be able to enter the space behind the rib, and this rib of the collector will be wasted. The drawings show the vertical layout based on the bottom limit of the collector being the top of the shoe plate. This can be varied by moving the collector down on the wall (as long as continuous blocking is supplied across the top as a fastener base), or up on the wall (as long as continuous blocking is supplied across the bottom as a fastener base).

Lay out the locations of the top and bottom of the collector vertically on the wall, using the actual height of the collector found in the introduction. Snap a chalk line across the studs at these points. Snap another chalk line horizontally across the studs, 3¾ in. inside the top and 6¼ in. inside the bottom of the collector. These lines are the upper and lower boundaries of the collector sheathing and the absorber plate. There must be solid continuous blocking from the outer lines, to ¾ in. inside the inner lines (3-W1).

The line chalked 6¼ in. above the bottom boundary will be the centerline of the lowest horizontal 2 x 6 (nominal) blocking, shown as the shoe plate on the drawings (2-W1). This blocking will be in a continuous straight line from one outer manifold stud to the other. Since the blocking will not be staggered, toe-nail the blocking at one end. Make sure the 1½ in. face of the blocking is flush with the outer face of the studs. Fasten a 2 x 4 (nominal) continuous line of blocking below the 2 x 6 (nominal), with its 3½ in. face flush with the outer face of the studs if there is no blocking there already.

Measure from the centerline of the 2 x 6 (nominal) blocking a distance equal to the "coverage" width (44 in. for 4-in. rib, 48 in. for 8-in. rib) of industrial sheet siding that will be used as the absorber plate. Fasten the centerline of a line of 2 x 4 (nominal) blocking here, with its 3½-in. face flush with the outer face of the studs. Again, the blocking joints will not be staggered, so toe-nail one end. Do *not* fasten this blocking in the manifold bays.

Continue this blocking up the face of the studs with the on-center distance equal to the width of the absorber plate sheets, until the top of the collector is reached. Block behind the top of the collector from the outer chalk line to a point ¾ in. below the inner chalk line.

A slot must be cut for the duct collars (Section 5.3) in the manifold bays through the bottom 2 x 6 (nominal) blocking and/or shoe plate. Cut the 2-in.-wide slot, 2½ in. back from the outer face of the studs, from manifold stud to manifold stud. Make the cut through the sub-floor as well (2, 3-W1). Fit 1-in.-thick pieces of rigid fiberglass against the band joist below the manifold bays. This will lessen the heat loss from the duct connection. If the lowest piece of 2 x 6 (nominal) blocking is above the shoe plate, fit insulation between that blocking and the shoe plate.

If the wall is built on a slab, the duct collar entrance (4-W2) must be made through the inside surface of the wall rather than through the floor. The duct collar would be attached on one end to the back side of the manifold pan, and on the other to a duct that would run against the wall. The duct can be finished to match the finish of the living space, or insulated if it is in a utility space.

> **RETROFIT:** Carefully cut slots in the plates within the manifold bays, ¾ in. back from the front face of the studs. Be careful to leave ¾ in. of shoe plate in front and in back of the slot. Carefully chisel away ¾ in. of the band joist width below the slot.

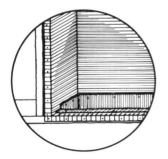

5.3 MANIFOLD PANS

The purpose of the manifold pans is to distribute air the full height of the collector. The supply and return ducts are connected to the pans. The air from the supply duct flows through the duct collar (4-W2) and fills the manifold pan, supplying the air to the full height of the collector. At the return manifold side, the hot air from behind the absorber plate will first fill the return manifold pan, and then be drawn away by the duct collar at the

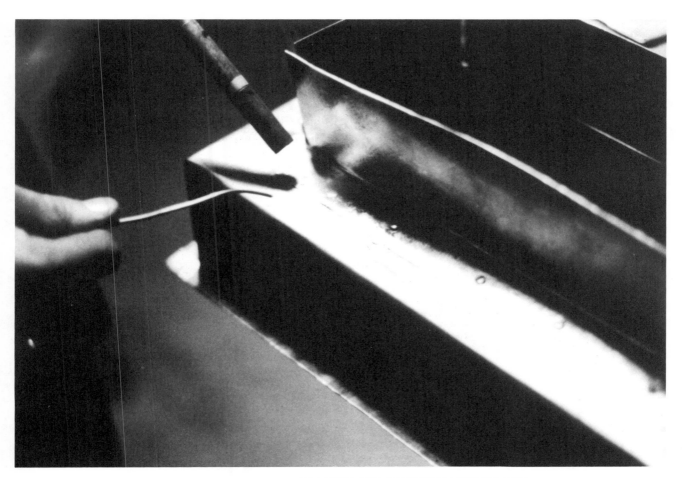

FIG. 5.2 SOLDERING THE DUCT COLLAR TO THE MANIFOLD PAN

bottom of the pan. The duct collars must be connected to the manifold pans with an airtight seal, or leakage will occur, and performance will be lost.

Prefabricate the manifold pans and duct collar inserts to the dimensions determined in Section 3.1. Have them made of 30-gauge galvanized sheet metal, with 1½-in. nailing flanges. Overlap the horizontal corners over the vertical corners. Solder all joints and all overlaps.

Decide which manifold will be closest to the storage rock bin (or living area to be heated directly). Make the return duct connection opening in that manifold pan, so that the duct run will

caulk, but also with support from studs and horizontal blocking. Caulk is also applied around the nailing flanges of the manifold pans, so that air cannot leak between the pans and the sheathing.

Thermo-Ply Collector Sheathing

Thermo-ply Super Strength (Blue) sheathing (⅛-in. foil-faced structural/insulative sheathing) is shown as the collector sheathing on the drawings. (See Appendix A.)

It is important that the four edges of the sheathing be supported by either blocking or the studs, horizontally and vertically. This is for structural reasons, and to minimize air leakage between the sheets of sheathing and the back of the collector.

The collector sheathing will run horizontally from the outside edge of one outer manifold stud to the outside edge of the other, and vertically from the centerline of the bottom 2 x 6 (nominal) to a point above it equal to the height of the glazing *minus* 1 in. Fasten with 1-in. galvanized roofing nails or $^7/_{16}$-in. crown divergent staples at 4 in. on center around the panel edges, and 8 in. on center at the intermediate supports. Run a continuous bead of caulk along the edge of each sheet before butting the edge of another against it. Begin fastening the sheets from the centerline of the collector. If the collector has center manifolds, cut manifold slots in the sheet to each side of the center stud before mounting the sheets on the wall. Use a plumb bob to make sure that the sheets are being fastened vertically.

Cut the sheets so that the edges fall over the studs or over the blocking. Measure and cut the widths of the two end sheets, but cut the manifold slots in them before mounting on the wall. Apply a ¼-in. continuous bead of urethane caulk around the edge of the manifold pan nailing flanges just before laying a sheet of Thermo-ply over them (3-A3). It is vital not to apply this caulk until you are ready to lay a sheet of sheathing over it. The caulk will harden quickly, especially on hot sunny days, and must be replaced if it skins over before the sheathing goes on. (See Appendix A for urethane caulk recommendations.)

be the shortest possible. The duct connection opening and duct collar should be sized according to Section 3.1. If there are four manifolds, the return duct connection should be in the two inner manifold bays, and the supply duct connections in the two outer manifold bays.

Place the manifold pans into the manifold bays, with the nailing flanges over the studs. Fasten the pans with 1-in. galvanized roofing nails at 6 in. on center around the nailing flanges (3, 4-W2).

Cut 1-in. rigid fiberglass insulation to fit snugly behind the band joists in the manifold bays. Insert the insulation before installing the duct collars (new construction only).

There are two ways to fasten the duct collar inserts to the manifold pans. One is to drop the inserts into the pans, and solder the insert to the pan. The other is to lay a ¼-in. continuous bead of caulk around the duct connection openings inside the manifold pans, and drop the duct collar inserts into the openings (2, 3-R2). Fasten with #6 x ¼ in. Phillips pan head sheet metal screws at 6 in. on center.

RETROFIT: If the room behind the collector is finished, a piece of ¾-in.-thick fiberglass insulation that will fit behind the manifold pan must be placed in the manifold bay before the pan. Cut the piece just big enough that it will fit snugly in the bay. Wedge it into the back of the manifold bay, and place the manifold pan in front of it.

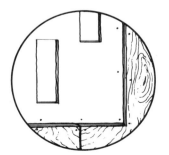

5.4 SHEATHING

The air from the supply manifold pan flows through slots cut in the collector sheathing (1-W3). The air flows across the face of the collector, between the sheathing and the absorber plate. Therefore, the seams between the sheathing must be airtight, to keep the air from leaking through the back of the collector. For the same reason, the edge of the collector sheathing and the roof sheathing must be airtight. This is accomplished with

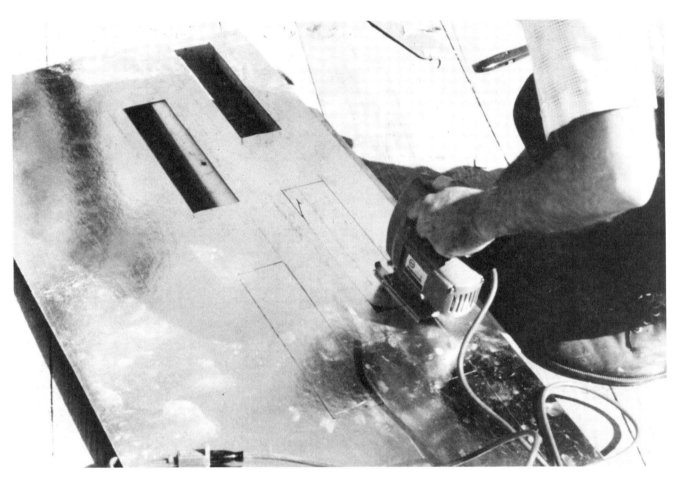

FIG. 5.3 CUTTING THE MANIFOLD SLOTS

Manifold Slots

Cut manifold slots in those sheets of Thermo-ply that will lay
over manifold pans. The slots are cut in the pattern called out so
that every rib in the absorber plate will be fed air from the
manifold pan. Measure in 3 in. from the outside edge of the
sheet and snap a chalk line parallel to the side and running the
length of the sheet. If the collector has center manifolds, cut
manifold slots in the two sheets that will go over the manifolds,
treating the side along the collector centerline as the "outside" of

FIG. 5.4 THERMO-PLY SHEATHING WITH MANIFOLD SLOTS

the sheet. Snap three more lines, parallel to the first and spaced 3 in. apart. Beginning at the centerline of the sheet and working first up and then down from it, mark the following lines between the pair of chalk lines closest to the edge of the sheet: 4½ in., 8 in., 9 in., 8 in., 9 in.

Beginning again at the centerline of the sheet and working first up and then down from it, mark the following lines between the pair of chalk lines *furthest* from the edge of the sheet: 4 in., 9 in., 8 in., 9 in., 8 in. Mark one line 2 in. inside the top and bottom edge of the Thermo-ply (2-W3). With a sabre saw or utility knife, carefully cut out the rectangles that measure 3 x 9 in., and the odd-shaped rectangle at the top and the bottom of the inner set. Repeat this process on the other end sheet of sheathing (and the center sheets, if there are center manifolds), and fasten them to the wall, as described in the section above (1, 3-W3).

In the sheet of Thermo-ply over the return manifold (the manifold closest to storage), drill one ⅛-in.-diameter hole for every temperature sensor to be used (1-W3). These holes will be lined up with the absorber ribs, beginning with the bottom rib, one hole per rib. They should be located horizontally at a distance in from the side of the collector (or from the collector centerline, if the center manifolds are return manifolds) equal to the manifold pan plus 4 in. These holes are for the wires from the temperature sensors that will be attached to the Thermo-ply.

Temperature Sensors

There are two temperature sensors that will be located near the return manifold pan. The first one is for controlling the normal operation of the collector. The second is for the overheating alarm. These sensors are mandatory. The third sensor, which operates the domestic hot water mode, should be mounted only if there is to be a DHW preheating system. Attach each one to the Thermo-ply located next to each hole drilled for the sensor wires (1-W3). Each sensor should be fastened according to manufacturer's instructions. Attach wires to the sensors if they are not already attached. Check the manufacturer's specifications for the type of wire, because some sensors require shielded

FIG. 5.5 DRILLING A HOLE FOR TEMPERATURE SENSOR WIRE

wire. Fasten the bottom edge of the sheet to the wall. Tie a knot
in each wire and position it over its respective 1/8-in.-diameter
hole in the Thermo-ply (3-W5). This will keep the wires from
being pulled out of the sensors, after the wires are fed through
the holes. Feed the wires through each hole, and then caulk the
holes in the Thermo-ply. Write with a felt marker on the back
side of the Thermo-ply which sensor is which (e.g. "T_C" for normal winter operation, T_{HL1} for overheating protection, and
"T_{CHW}" for DHW control).

FIG. 5.6 THERMO-PLY SHEATHING AND MANIFOLD SLOTS IN PLACE

Wall Sheathing

Sheathe the rest of the wall as usual, with ½-in. CDX plywood,
caulking continuously between the edges of the collector sheathing and the wall sheathing (2-W3). Mark the centerline of the
collector on the wall sheathing, 4 in. *above* and *below* the

Thermo-ply perimeter. If the collector has inner manifold pans, snap a chalk line down the centerline of the collector between the two pairs of manifold slots.

RETROFIT: Sheathe the wall, as above. The Thermo-ply will run horizontally from the outside of one outer manifold stud to the other, and vertically from the centerline of the bottom 2 x 6 (nominal) blocking (or shoe) to a point above it at a distance equal to the glazing height *minus* 1 in. (the two inside lines snapped horizontally on the sheathing). This will leave a 2-in. gap at each side, 3¾ in. at the top, and 6¼ in. at the bottom, between the Thermo-ply and the existing wall sheathing. Cut ½ in. CDX plywood to fill these gaps, caulking each side edge of the plywood as it goes in.

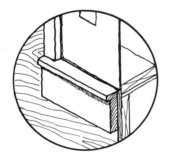

5.5 PERIMETER BLOCKING

The perimeter blocking not only sets the boundaries for the absorber plate to be fastened within, but is also the beginning of the framework of the glazing. It is vital that these pieces be plumb, horizontal, and square—and be fastened to the exact dimensions required. Therefore, follow the sequence of laying out, plumbing, leveling, and checking diagonals carefully. Check the dimensions several times to be sure they are correct. Any miscalculation now could mean the glass won't fit later.

TOP. Tack 1 x 2 (nominal) blocking across the top edge of the collector, with its bottom edge flush with the edge of the plywood. The blocking will run continuously from 2 in. outside one side of the Thermo-ply to 2 in. outside the other (1, 3-W4). Use a line level to make *sure* the blocking is horizontal.

SIDES. Tack ¾ x 2 in. (actual) blocking down the sides of the collector, with its side flush with the side edge of the plywood. The blocking will run continuously from the bottom edge of the top perimeter blocking to the bottom edge of the Thermo-ply (1, 2-W4). Use a plumb bob to be *sure* the blocking is vertical.

BOTTOM. Cut a ½ x 4¾ in. (actual) continuous rectangular section from a 2 x 6 (nominal) (3-W4). The L-shaped piece will run continuously from the outside edge of one side perimeter blocking to the outside edge of the other. Tack the piece across the bottom, with its top edge flush with the edge of the plywood. Use a line level to make sure the blocking is horizontal.

It is essential that these pieces are square with each other, so that the glass will fit later. Check the diagonals from the *outside* corners of the perimeter blocking. The bottom outside corners of the *batten shelf* cut out of the bottom 2 x 6 (nominal) blocking will be considered the bottom outside corners of the diagonals (3-W4).

The vertical height from the bottom edge of the batten shelf to the top edge of the 1 x 2 (nominal) blocking should equal the glazing height plus ½ in. Without this extra ½-in. space (¼ in. allowed for above and below the glass), the glass will crack when it expands. The horizontal distance must be equal to the width of the collector, which takes into account the expansion spaces needed for the panels of glass. Therefore, the blocking must be fastened to the required dimensions, as well as have equal diagonals.

5.6 ABSORBER PLATE

The air from the supply manifold pan passes through the manifold slots in the Thermo-ply into the ribs of the absorber plate. It flows between the back surface of the plate's ribs and the face of the Thermo-ply, carrying away the heat from the two surfaces as it passes by. It then is pulled through the slots into the return manifold pan. The absorber plate is painted black to absorb more of the sun's light, and reflect less back to the outside.

It is very important that every edge of the absorber plate, including the overlaps, be airtight. Leakage through the absorber plate can mean the difference between a good collector and a poor one. Therefore, be generous with the urethane caulk, and don't skimp on the screws. The number specified will help keep the aluminum expansion to a minimum. The less the plate moves, the longer the seal of the caulk will hold.

The absorber plate is made of 4-in. or 8-in. ribbed aluminum industrial siding sheets. If the collector is less than 12 feet from inner supply manifold slot to inner return manifold slot, use 4-in. rib. If the collector is equal to or greater than 12 feet, use 8-in. rib. The 4-in. rib comes in 45⅝ in. overall widths, which actually cover 44 inches. The 8-in. rib comes in 49⅝ in. overall widths, which actually cover 48 inches.

Decide which sheet width will be used, and order it in the .032-in. thickness with the mill finish. (Construction drawings show 8-in. rib sheets.) Enough sheets will be needed to cover the collector vertically from the bottom to the top edge of the Thermo-ply (3-W5). The sheets will be as long as the horizontal distance from side to side of the Thermo-ply (2-W5). Use the following two equations to determine the number of sheets to order, and their length:

No. of sheets (round off to the next highest whole number) = (glazing height in inches −1 in.) / 48 in. (for 8 in. rib) or 44 in. (for 4 in. rib)
Sheet width (round off to the next highest 6 in.) = (collector width in inches −4 in.)

For example, if the collector were the same one used as the example in the introduction (15'10½" wide x 8'9" high) and the 8-in. rib sheets were being used, the number of sheets ordered would be:

(96" − 1")/48" = 1.98 or 2 sheets.

If the 4-in. rib sheets were being used, the number of sheets ordered would be:

(96" − 1")/44" = 2.16 or 3 sheets.

Notice the amount of aluminum that would be wasted if the 4-in. rib sheet is used. Only 6½ in. of the last sheet would be used.

In either case, the sheet width to order would be:
(15'10½" − 4") = 15'6½".

The sheets come in standard lengths up to 30 feet, in increments of 6 inches. If the collector is longer than 30 feet, divide

the collector width in half and use two sheets to cover the width.
The sheets will butt together at the centerline of the collector,
between the two inner manifold pans.

At the ends of each sheet there will be a high temperature,
pure EPDM end closure strip. Order enough "inside" end closure strips by the linear foot to close off all the ends of the
sheets. For example, if the collector is one sheet wide, order two
times the height of the collector. If it is two sheets wide, order

FIG. 5.7 SIDING AND EPDM END CLOSURE STRIPS

FIG. 5.8 CUTTING AN ABSORBER PLATE ALONG THE RIB

four times the height, because there will be two sets of EPDM
end closure strips at the centerline of the collector.

The sheets of siding will be fastened with the rib running horizontally across the collector, and the 1⅜-in. rib valley fastened
against the Thermo-ply (3-W5).

The sheets will probably have to be cut both horizontally and
vertically. Horizontal and vertical cuts can be made with a

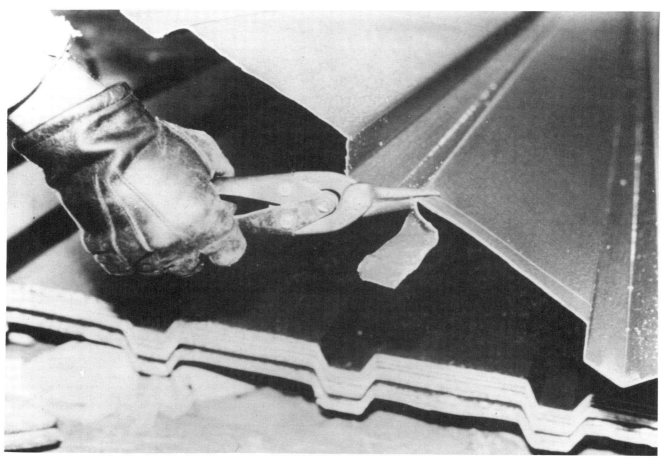

FIG. 5.9 CUTTING AN ABSORBER PLATE ACROSS THE RIB

handheld circular saw (using a carbide blade). Cuts across the
rib can also be made with a pair of tin snips. Cuts along the rib
or rib valley can be scored with a utility knife; the siding is then
bent back and forth until the metal breaks clean. When using
the circular saw, wear eye and ear protection, as well as a
respiration mask, while cutting. Cutting the sheet may raise or
bend the edge slightly. Remove the raised edges with a file or
utility knife, and straighten the edge with a pair of pliers.

Cut the sheets to the length required to fit horizontally across
the collector (e.g. 15'6½"). Save a full piece of ribbed scrap, cut
from the end of one sheet, to be used later. Cut off ⅜ in. from

the bottom horizontal edge of the first sheet of siding, removing the curved portion and leaving ¾ in. of flat metal rib valley before the rib begins. The top of the last sheet will be cut after all the other sheets are in place on the wall and an actual measurement can be taken.

Sheet Preparation

To remove the thin film of oil that will be found on the sheets and prepare them for painting, sponge down the outside of the sheets with a solution of trisodium-phosphate (TSP) powder dissolved in water. Next, etch the sheets with muriatic acid according to manufacturer's instructions. The TSP powder and the muriatic acid are both available at hardware or building supply stores.

Using the scrap piece of siding as a guide, and a ¼-in. continuous bead of urethane caulk as the adhesive, lay out and stick the end closure strips for the first sheet of ribbed siding to the wall (2-W5). The caulk must still be wet for it to act like a glue, so don't let it skim over before pushing the closure strips into it. Fit the ribs of the closure strip into the ribs in the scrap piece. Following the form of the siding will keep the closure strip from becoming stretched out as it is inserted into the caulk. Begin at the bottom perimeter seam between the Thermo-ply and the plywood, and line the strips up with the side seams of the Thermo-ply.

If the collector has center manifolds, run one strip down each side of the collector centerline (the seam in the Thermo-ply). Do not let the caulk skim over before covering it with the strips. If it does, remove it and caulk again.

Just before the first sheet is ready to be fastened to the wall, run a ¼-in. continuous bead of caulk over the inside top edge of the EPDM end closure strips. Run the same size continuous bead across the bottom of the collector, along the bottom perimeter seam. Butt the bottom edge of the first sheet against the edge of the plywood at the perimeter of the collector, laying the sheet carefully over the end closure strips (3-W5). Make sure the end closure strips fit snugly into the ribs.

FIG. 5.11 LAYING OUT EPDM END CLOSURE STRIPS
WITH A SCRAP LENGTH OF SIDING

Fasten the sheet across the bottom edge, with #12 x 1¼-in. Phillips pan head aluminum or 18-8 stainless steel sheet metal screws at 6 in. on center. Fasten vertically through every rib valley at the ends of the sheet, and through every other rib valley at every stud (for 4-in. rib; for 8-in. rib, fasten into every rib valley). The studs can be found by noticing where the nails or staples are in the Thermo-ply. *Do not* fasten across the top of the sheet yet.

Lay out and caulk the EPDM end closure strips for the next sheet. Apply extra caulk where these strips butt against those already on the wall. Run a ¼-in. continuous bead of caulk

FIG. 5.10 WASHING THE ABSORBER PLATE

FIG. 5.12 CAULKING THE EPDM END CLOSURE STRIP

across the top edge of the overlap strip of the sheet already on the wall—at the top edge of the top rib valley (3-R5). Place the bottom rib valley of the second sheet over it. Position the second sheet over the end closure strips. Wipe off any caulk that has been forced out before it skins over. Follow the same fastening schedule as on the first sheet. Continue this process for all sheets except the top one.

Once the second-to-last sheet is on, measure from the bottom edge of the last rib valley to the top perimeter seam between the Thermo-ply and the plywood. This distance will be the width to cut the last sheet. If the top of the last sheet is cut across a rib valley, follow the layout of the end closure strips and the same fastening schedule as the other sheets. Run a ¼-in. continuous bead of caulk along the bottom edge of the Thermo-ply. Lay the ribbed siding over it and fasten at 6 in. on center.

If the top edge of the last sheet is cut across a rib, follow the layout of the end closure strips and the same fastening schedule as the last sheets. Cut a continuous piece of 1 x 1 in. (actual) fir or spruce blocking. Run a ¼-in. continuous bead of caulk along the top perimeter edge of the Thermo-ply. Lay the continuous blocking in the caulk, and butt its length against the side

FIG. 5.13 PAINTING THE ABSORBER PLATE

FIG. 5.14 ABSORBER PLATE POSITIONED ON WALL

of the plywood edge, and against the end closure strips at each end. Caulk again along the top edge of the blocking and lay the edge of the last sheet over it. Fasten with #12 x 2½-in. Phillips pan head aluminum or 18-8 stainless steel metal screws at 6 in. on center.

Check the four corners of the collector. The end closure strips may raise the ends of the top and bottom edges slightly, which will cause leaks. If necessary, loosen the screws, add more caulk, then tighten and add more screws.

Priming and Painting

Prime and paint the absorber plate according to paint manufacturer's instructions. (See Appendix A for recommendations.) Paint the inside surfaces of any wood exposed around the perimeter of the plate, with one coat of each, also. Allow the

paint to dry completely, a minimum of two full days. Standard
enamel paints dry by solvent evaporation, a process that should
be allowed to finish before the glazing goes on. If there is not
enough time to allow for this, an epoxy based paint must be
used. Once the absorber plate is painted, be careful not to
scratch it. Precautions should be taken, such as wrapping ladder legs (if used) with rags. Touch up any scratches with paint,
before the glazing is installed.

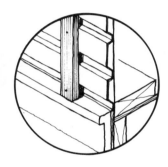

5.7 BATTENS

The battens are those vertical members to which the glazing
system is attached, so they must be securely fastened to the
absorber plate or the side blocking. They must also be plumb,
and the exact distance apart, or the glass will not fit. Check the
dimensions, plumb, and diagonals carefully, then check again.

Cut 1 x 3 (nominal) fir or spruce battens (1-W6) whose heights
are equal to the glazing height *minus* 1 in. Paint with two
coats of flat black paint. (See Appendix A for paint recommendations.)

Tack the two outside battens down the sides of the collector
first, lining up their outside edges with the outside edge of the
perimeter blocking. Use a plumb bob to be sure the battens are
vertical (2-W6). The outside-to-outside dimension should equal
the collector width. Cut a piece of plywood with a horizontal
dimension equal to the glazing width minus 1½". This is used as
a guide to make sure the battens will be the correct distance
from each other, so be sure the dimensions are exact, especially
at the corners.

Fasten the first vertical batten down the centerline of the collector. Check the diagonals to be sure it is square with the
perimeter battens. Lay out the battens to each side, fastening
down each batten as the plywood guide is run down between it
and the one already fastened next to it. Fasten with #14 x 1½
in. aluminum or 18-8 stainless steel Phillips flat head wood
screws through every other rib (4-in. rib; every rib for 8-in. rib).
By the time the last one is laid out, the plywood guide should fit

between this batten and the one preceeding it, and between this same batten and the one fastened to the perimeter blocking. Fasten the two outside battens with 3-in. drywall screws at 1′0″ on center. The outside edges of the two outside battens should be flush with the outside edges of the perimeter blocking.

FIG. 5.15 FASTENING THE CENTER BATTEN

FIG. 5.16 BATTENS IN PLACE ON COLLECTOR

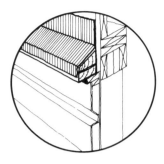

5.8 GLAZING PREPARATION

The glazing preparation consists of several important parts. The first is weatherproofing the top and sides of the collector perimeter with blocking and flashing. The blocking, or cant set, across the top of the collector is sloped to allow for drainage. The second step is fabricating and attaching the sill, the piece of wood that will bear the weight of the glass. This sill is cut with channels that will allow condensation to escape from between the glazing and the absorber plate. The sill must be securely fastened, for each double panel of glass can weigh from 72 pounds (34 x 76 in.) to 120 pounds (46 x 96 in.). Before it is fastened, check and double-check its position. The dimension from its top surface to the bottom surface of the cant set must equal the glass height plus ½ in. Too small, and the glass might not fit, or worse it might crack later when it expands in the heat.

The smoke test is vital to the performance of the collector. The collector must be thoroughly checked for leaks. As will be seen on the first test, no matter how well the collector was caulked, there will still be spots that were missed. But don't get discouraged—the leaks are not difficult to seal. More than one test, however, will surely be needed to find and seal them all.

The pre-shimmed glazing tape acts not only as a seal between the edge of the glass and the interior of the collector, but also as a cushion against wind pressure.

The glazing will be protected around the collector perimeter by a cant strip and blocking set across the top, and blocking down the sides. Across the bottom it is protected and supported by a sill. It is held out from the battens with pre-shimmed glazing tape (1-W7).

Blocking

CANT STRIP. The cant strip and blocking set consists of two 2 x 3s (nominal), the top piece ripped across the long side with a side angle cut at a minimum of 4 in 12 (18.5°). The blocking and cant strip extend to the outside edges of the side battens. Tack the first 2 x 3 (nominal) across the top of the perimeter blocking, with its 1½ in. face against the plywood sheathing. Tack the cant

FIG. 5.17 THE CANT SET

strip above the blocking with its 2½-in. face flush with the 2½-in. face of the blocking (3-W7).

SIDE BLOCKING. Tack 1 x 1¾ in. (actual) continuous blocking down the sides of the collector with the outside edges flush with the outer edges of the battens. The blocking will run from the underside of the cant strip set, and its height is equal to the height of the glazing plus 6 in. The clear distance from inside to inside of this blocking must be equal to the collector width minus 3½ in. to allow for glass expansion (2-W7).

FIG. 5.18 SIDE BLOCKING

Sill

The 2 x 6 (nominal) finish-grade cedar sill will run horizontally across the bottom of the collector, from inside to inside of the side blocking. The top edge of the blocking will fit into the rectangular notch in the bottom perimeter blocking. Its top edge must be at a distance down from the cant strip set equal to the glazing height plus ½ inch (1-W7).

The sill should be prepared before mounting with ¼-in.-square condensation and drip channels set back ½ in. from its front face. Rout out the horizontal channel. Cut 1-in.-deep by ½-in.-wide vertical saw kerfs from the back of the sill at 1'0" on center, beginning at the centerline of the sill (3-W7). The kerf shall be continuous from channel to channel.

FIG. 5.19 SILL FOR GLAZING SUPPORT

Tack the sill across the bottom of the collector, using a line
level to be sure it is horizontal. Check the dimensions from the
inside edge of the cant strip set to the inside edge of the sill, at
several points. The clear distance must equal the glazing height
plus ½ in. all the way across to allow for glass expansion.
Check the diagonals also, as well as plumb and level lines.

Once the pieces are square, fasten the 2 x 3 (nominal) top
blocking with 30d common nails at 1'0" on center, and the cant
strip with 10d common nails at the same spacing. Fasten the
side blocking with 16d common nails at 1'0" on center. Fasten
the sill with ½ x 4 in. hexhead lag screws, countersunk, at 1'0"
on center. Do not fasten the lag screws through any of the weep
slots.

Flashing

Bend 10-in.-wide 0.019 in. aluminum flashing around the side
blocking and onto the wall, beginning at the centerline of the
side blocking. Start at a point 1¾ in. below the top of the sill,
and carry the flashing up the side, bending over the end of the
cant strip. Fasten with 1-in. galvanized roofing nails at 1'0" on
center.

Bend 10-in.-wide 0.019 in. aluminum flashing around the cant
strip and up the wall, beginning at the centerline of the 2 x 3
(nominal) blocking across the top of the collector. The flashing
should be continuous from one side of the collector to the other.
Bend the flashing over the wall with 1-in. galvanized roofing
nails at 1'0" on center.

Smoke Test

Before installing the glazing tape, or the glazing, it is necessary
to check for leaks in the system. *This is important*, since even
small leaks will reduce the efficiency of the collector dramatically. One method of checking for leaks is a smoke test. This
can be done using a metal can and a smoke bomb. (See *Appendix A* for recommendations.) Follow the manufacturer's
warnings.

It is helpful at this point to have the supply and return ducts attached to the duct collars, to check for leaks at the connections.

Seal off the duct connections to one manifold or duct, using polyethylene film (or cardboard) and duct tape. Leave the other manifold duct temporarily open to put the can through. Place the smoke bomb in a paint or soft drink can, ignite it, and place it into the duct. Seal the opening. Carefully check the collector for leaks, and seal all leaks with caulk.

It will not be unusual for the collector to leak slightly around the edges of the absorber plate and at the overlaps, and these leaks must be completely sealed. Adding extra clear silicone caulk and more screws at these seams will help stop the leaks. Paint over any new screws and touch up any scratches.

Also check the back of the collector for leaks at the manifolds or ducts, or leaks caused by any fasteners that punctured the Thermo-ply. Caulk all leaks with silicone caulk.

Several tests may be required before all the leaks are sealed.

Just before glazing each bay with an insulated glass panel, run ⅛ x ½-in. pre-shimmed glazing tape vertically down the inside edges of the front face of the battens, horizontally across the bottom edges of the front face of the top perimeter blocking, and the top edge of the front face of the batten shelf (2, 3-W7).

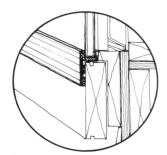

5.9 GLAZING AND FINISHING

The insulated glass panels allow the sun's light to pass through and hit the absorber plate, but slow the transfer of the resulting heat back to the outside. The glass must be able to expand and contract freely with the extreme temperature changes. Therefore, the ¼-in. gap allowed around each panel is vital to the survival of the glass. Each panel of glass rests on two setting blocks. These blocks support both pieces of glass, but allow each to move independently with expansion and contraction. The inner layer of glass will move much more than the outer, because it is experiencing higher temperatures. This is the reason why insulating glass panels with metal or glass fused edges cannot be used. Only flexible sealed units can be used.

The aluminum clamping bars with built-in gaskets provide support, along with an *almost* caulk-free, weatherproof seal. The only place caulk is needed is at the intersections of the clamping bars, where water could leak in under the bars and rot the wood.

Glazing

The rest of the glazing process involves mounting insulated glass panels to the collector with the CY/RO Universal Glazing System. (See Appendix A.) The total CY/RO U.G.S. consists of a lower EPDM gasket, an aluminum clamping bar and two upper EPDM gaskets. The lower gasket has been replaced on the wall collector by pre-shimmed glazing tape, so do not order the lower gasket (4-W8).

Cut two sections of the clamping bar 1 in. longer than the width of the collector (from outside edge to outside edge of the side blocking) for the top and bottom. Miter the corners so that the outside length of the bars equals the width of the collector. Cut two sections of the clamping bar, 1 in. longer than the height of the collector (equal to the glazing height in inches plus 4¼ in.), for the two sides of the collector. Miter the corners so that the outside height of the bars equals the glazing height, plus 3¼ inches. Cut the rest of the vertical clamping bars, to be placed over the battens, the height of the glazing minus 1½ in. (1-W8).

If the collector is wider than 25 feet, the horizontal bars may have to be done in pieces. The clamping bar only comes in stock sizes of 25-foot lengths. Try to keep the splices to a minimum.

Predrill the clamping bars at 8 in. on center along the centerline of the bars, with holes no more than ½ in. from the ends. Feed the upper gaskets into the channels extruded into the under side of the bars. Run the gaskets continuously through any splices of the clamping bars.

Line up the bottom horizontal clamping bar along the sill, with its top edge ¾ in. above the top edge of the sill. Fasten with #12 x 2-in. aluminum or 18-8 stainless steel Phillips pan head sheet metal screws, with neoprene washers. Fasten all the screws partway, leaving enough room to set the glass on the sill without disturbing the glazing tape. Repeat this process up one side of the collector, lining up the inside edge ¾ in. to the inside of the inner face of the perimeter blocking.

SETTING BLOCKS. Each panel of glass will be centered between vertical strips of glazing tape. Place two ¼ x ¼ x 4-in. neoprene (80-90 Shore-A-Durometer) setting blocks on the sill at the quarter points of each of the bays (1, 3-W8). The setting blocks are available from local glazing dealers.

GLASS INSTALLATION. Special precautions must be taken when handling large panes of insulated glass. If a unit is leaned against a vertical support, provide one support under both panes of glass to keep them from sliding apart. Take care not to damage the edges, and do not pivot the glass panels on their corners. The glazing recommended in Appendix A comes with a stencil in one corner. This stencil should be glazed to the inside bottom lefthand corner when installed. Clean the inside of the glass thoroughly before pressing the glass into place against the tape.

In the corner framed by the two clamping bars, place glazing tape and carefully slide the first panel of glass underneath the two glazing bars. Center the glass inside the boundaries set by the clamping bar and the batten, lining up the free edge with the edge of the glazing tape nearest the centerline of the batten. (The glass *must* be ½ in. from the centerline of the batten.) Tighten the screws on the two clamping bars already in place. Center the next vertical clamping bar over the next batten, covering the free edges of the glass. Partially fasten the screws. Do not fasten the top clamping bar at this time.

Center the next panel of glass in the same way. Fasten the screws across the bottom of the glass, and up the batten between the two panels. Partially fasten the next vertical clamping bar to the batten. Continue this process across the collector until the last vertical clamping bar is fully fastened. Fasten the top horizontal batten across the collector, overlapping the clamping bar ¾ in. over the glass.

Caulk all the intersections of the clamping bars: horizontal and vertical joints, splices and mitered corners. This will keep water from leaking through the intersections and under the clamping bars.

Interior Finishing

Cut rigid fiberglass insulation the width and length necessary to fit behind the manifold pans, from manifold stud to manifold stud, and from top to bottom blocking. Make the insulation as thick as will fit, without protruding beyond the studs. Locate the sensor wires that were fed through the Thermo-ply. Attach each sensor wire to its respective control, and attach each control near the back of the collector. Future access to the controls and to the sensors may be necessary (by cutting through the back of the Thermo-ply, replacing sensor, and duct-taping the cutout in place again).

Attach more wire (shielded wire if manufacturer calls for it), and run to the air-handling control panel (see Figures 1.17 and 7.18 or 7.25 and 7.28 and 7.29). It is important to tag the wires so that they don't become confused with each other. Insulate between the other studs with full depth fiberglass batt insulation. Staple a 6-mil polyethylene vapor barrier to the studs, overlapping the sheets 6 in. and taping the edges. Finish the interior surface as desired.

CHAPTER 6

BUILDING
THE ROCK BIN

A rock bin is needed for those systems that require remote storage: systems whose collector areas are too large to be connected directly to the living space. If the collector is too large, it produces more heat than the living space can use. This excess heat can be carried to a storage bin, stored in the mass of the rocks, and later retrieved as needed.

Most rock bins are built with a duct opening at the top and a duct opening at the bottom. Hot air from the collector is introduced at the top, forced down through the rocks and out the bottom. The MODEL-TEA rock bin differs from these because the duct openings are both at the top. A center partition with an air space below it allows the air to enter at the top duct opening on one side, pass down through the rocks, slip under the partition, and pass up through the rocks on the other side. The U-shaped rock bin coined its name from the U-shaped air flow pattern (See Figure 6.2).

The U-shaped rock bin is divided into two equal halves by the center partition or divider, and there is one duct opening on each side of the divider. The side connected to the return duct from the collector is called the *hot side*, because the rocks on this side receive the heat first and will be the first to warm up. The side connected to the supply duct to the collector is called the *cold side*. The rocks here stay cold until the rocks on the hot side have stored all the heat they can, at which time the heat in the air is carried to the cold side of the rock bin and begins heating these rocks.

The U-shaped rock bin is divided into three parts vertically: the rocks themselves, and two air plenums. The first air plenum is above the rocks, where the air enters from the duct. The air fills the whole plenum first and then begins to move down through the rocks. The rocks rest on a row of concrete bond blocks, which form the second plenum. The concrete bond blocks have a special core that, when placed at a right angle to the center divider, guides the air under the rocks, under the divider and into the plenum under the other side of rocks.

Add the two plenums and the cover to the height of the rocks, and the rock bin is only 6'6" high, low enough to fit into most basements. The rock height was limited to 3'8" so that the rock bin would be suitable for new or retrofit construction.

FIG. 6.1 ROCK BIN UNDER CONSTRUCTION

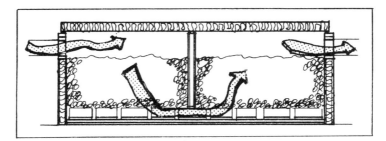

FIG. 6.2 AIR FLOW THROUGH THE U-SHAPED ROCK BIN

The instructions on how to build the U-shaped rock bin are meant for those persons familiar with wood-frame construction—skilled contractors, carpenters, or owner-builders. The key word is skill, the ability to perform the tasks, based on working knowledge gained from carpentry experience. The more experience, the easier these instructions will be to follow.

This chapter, plus Chapter 4 or Chapter 5 on constructing the MODEL-TEA collector, and Chapter 7 on the MODEL-TEA System Control Wiring should all be read thoroughly before beginning to order materials or beginning any steps of construction.

The experienced carpenter will have most of the tools necessary to build this storage bin, but may have to borrow or rent a few of the specialized ones. Among the tools needed are:

hammers, screwdrivers, tapes, pliers, tin snips, chalk line, caulking gun, hand saws, circular saw, table saw, sabre saw, power screwdriver or variable speed/reversible drill, power-actuated setting device

The instructions are written for new construction applications, but there are special sections for any *additional* special instructions you need for retrofit.

RETROFIT: The instructions will begin with the word *RETROFIT* and these sections *must* be read by those who are retrofitting the rock bin; they may be skipped by those concerned only with new construction.

6.1 LOCATION AND SIZING

Before building the rock bin, certain calculations must be done and decisions reached. First, the rock bin must be sized according to the square footage of the collector. Table 3.1 gives cubic feet of rock figures for square feet of collector. Choose the proper collector square foot figure, and find the cubic feet of rock needed to store the energy from the collector.

Due to height limitations in typical basement construction, the actual height of the rocks in the bin is limited to 3'8". Divide the cubic feet of rock by 3.67, to determine the square feet of floor area of the rock. In specific site conditions, the length and width of the rock bin can vary to best fit in a certain location. The actual width and length of the bin must include the thicknesses of the walls, in addition to the width or length of rocks. By deciding the best rock dimension in one direction, and dividing it into the square foot area of rock, the rock dimension in the other direction can be found.

There will be two ducts entering the rock bin, and the square foot area of the rocks must be divided equally between them by a 2 x 4 (nominal) vertical wall with plywood on both sides. This wall must also be added into the width or length of the rock bin. Use the following two formulas to calculate the length of the walls parallel with the center partition (the parallel walls) and the walls perpendicular to the center partition (the perpendicular walls):

Parallel Walls = width in ft. of rock + 1'2"
Perpendicular Walls = length in ft. of rock + 1'2" + 4½"

Select the spot for the rock bin, and plan where the ducts will run. Choose which side will receive hot air from the collector and which side will be sending the cool air back to the collector. Label the hot and cold sides of the rock bin on the drawings. Write in the actual dimensions of the rock bin calculated.

Read through the drawings step by step with the instructions until everything is clear. The drawings are not meant to be used without the instructions, nor are the instructions meant to be used without the drawings. Make notes on the drawings of those things that depend on site conditions. Determine how much of each material needs to be ordered, and see the sources listed in Appendix A.2. Refer to the materials descriptions in Appendix A.1 as needed; such things as which type of caulk to use with which type of joint are discussed.

Note: It will be easier to load the rock bin with the rock, and to place and fasten the cover, if the floor framing is not begun until after the rock bin is complete. For retrofit, it is possible to construct the bin with the floor already in place, but it is more difficult.

Cover the rock bin with a sheet of 6-mil polyethylene when work is not being conducted on it. This will keep it dry until the building is closed in around it.

The step-by-step instructions are keyed to the construction drawings on the foldouts found elsewhere in this book. Each construction step has a key number, and a corresponding key sketch in the margin where the step begins. Each construction step has a corresponding drawing, with the same key sketch in the upper righthand drawing.

As you read each section, you will be asked to refer to details on the construction drawings. For example, you might see (4-B6) at the end of a sentence. This means "refer to detail 4, on bin drawing number 6. Turn to bin drawing number 6, and you will see a number 6 in the upper righthand corner with the word "bin" below it. The key sketch is there, as well as the title of the page and the step: Bracing and loading. As you refer back and forth from instructions to drawings, look for these four things: the drawing number, the word *Bin*, the key sketch and the title of the page. It is important that the instructions and the drawings are used together.

6.2 BUILDING PREPARATION

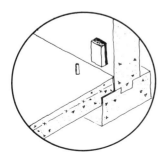

This section deals with locating the rock bin, and preparing the floor and walls to receive it. The location of the rock bin, and its relationship to the collector and the living space is an important step in good system design. Structurally, the building must be able to bear the load of the rocks, which will exert a tremendous load on its walls and on the floor slab. The rock bin must be built on a slab, because normal framing could never carry the load.

The rock bin should be located in a clear space big enough for the bin, with a clear area from 8 to 10 feet to one side of it. This space will be for the duct entry into the box and for the air handler and duct connections to it. The bin should be located so that duct runs from the collector and duct runs for air delivery to the living space are as short as possible. This will help reduce heat losses.

If the storage bin is placed against a foundation wall (or better yet, in a corner), the number of slab anchor bolts and amount of temporary bracing required for rock loading can be reduced.

RETROFIT: The discussion above applies to retrofit applications. In addition, place the bin in a spot that stays dry year-round. Moisture could rot the wood in the bin, as well as decrease system performance.

The spot where the bin is located should have first-floor joists high enough above the floor to allow someone to crawl over the top of the bin later. The area should be clear of low ductwork and piping.

Last, bear in mind where and how the rocks will be coming into the basement. If possible, try to minimize the distance between the point of entry and the rock bin. This will help save time and labor.

SLAB. The concrete floor slab under the rock bin, and 6 in. beyond its perimeter, should be 6 in. thick with 6 x 6 x 10/10 woven wire mesh at a level 2 in. below its surface.

ANCHOR BOLTS. Anchor bolts will be used along any walls that are "freestanding," or not beside the foundation walls. These walls will be called *bolt walls*. The anchor bolts will help hold the walls against spreading under the load of the rocks. The ½ x 8 in. bolts will be located 3 in. back from the exterior faces of the rock bin.

Beginning with the walls perpendicular to the foundation walls, measure out a distance from the foundation wall equal to the rock bin width (or length) minus 1 in. (1-B1). Place the bolts at 2'0" on center, moving back toward the foundation wall, with the last one 5 in. from the wall. Leave 2½ in. of the bolts exposed above the slab (2-B1).

If the wall is parallel to the foundation wall, but freestanding, place the bolts for the other two walls first, in lines that are the distance apart equal to the rock bin width or length minus 6 in. Then, at 2'0" on center, place a line of anchor bolts from one existing line to the other. These bolts should be at a distance from the foundation wall equal to the rock bin length (or width) minus 1 in.

RETROFIT: If the basement already has a slab, but is not 6 in. thick, pour another layer of concrete with wire mesh reinforcment, until it is a total of 6 in. minimum. Instead of using anchor bolts, shoot the shoe plates of the walls into the slab with powder-driven ¼ x 3$^7/_{16}$ in. pins at 2'0" on center.

SPACERS. Blocking will be used to brace the walls that stand next to the foundation walls against spreading under the load of the rocks (1-B1). These 2 x 4 (nominal) x 6 in. spacers should be treated with a wood preservative. Shoot them at 16 in. on center into the foundation wall in two rows, with powder driven ¼ x 3$^7/_{16}$ in. pins. Place a ½-in. liner of rigid insulation between each spacer and the wall. The insulation will keep the wood out of direct contact with moisture in the concrete. Fasten the spacers with the top of the higher row at 6'0" from the slab, and the top of the lower row at 6¾ in. from the slab (2-B1). These walls that will stand next to foundation walls will be called *spacer walls*.

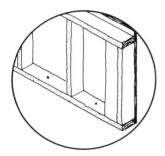

6.3 BIN PANELS

The rock bin will be built out of panels that are prefabricated and then tipped up into place. They are built according to normal wood-frame practices, with a few minor changes. The rock bin frame has six parts: four outside walls, a center partition, and a cover. The outside walls, or panels, are constructed in this section.

Studs

The rock bin walls will be built out of 2 x 6 (nominal) studs at 24 in. on center and sheathed on the outside with ½-in. CDX plywood. The panels should be framed with double studs in one corner, and a single stud at the other end, 6 in. from the end of the plywood (1-B2). This arrangement will allow for easy fastening of the panels from the inside, once the four panels are assembled. The shoe and the first top plates will run from the outside of the double stud to the outside of the single stud. The panels will be 6'0" high and their length will be the box width or length, minus ½ inch. Frame the top plate 1½ in. down from the top of the plywood (3, 4-B2).

All bolt walls will be framed across the shoe plate with framing hangers, with the outside of the hanger between the stud and the plywood. This will help keep the studs from sliding on

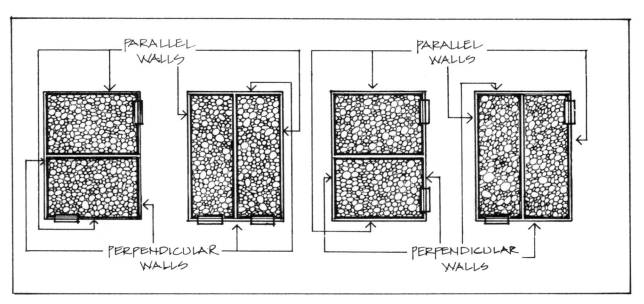

FIG. 6.3 RELATIONSHIP OF CENTER DIVIDER TO DUCT OPENINGS

the shoe plate under the load of the rocks (4-B2; panels C and D, 1-B2). Mark where the anchor bolts will be on the bolt wall shoe plate, and drill holes for the anchor bolts.

Where the duct openings will be, and in which walls, will depend on actual site conditions. But wherever they are located, the square foot area of the rock bin must be divided equally between them. This center partition will be called the *divider*, a 2 x 4 (nominal) stud wall that will frame between the two duct openings (See Figure 6.3).

At the centerline of the two panels *perpendicular* to the center divider, frame a 2 x 6 (nominal) with its 5½-in. face flush with the inner wall face, and a 2 x 6 (nominal) ripped to 4 in. perpendicular to its centerline (panels A and C, 1-B2). Edge-nail the 2 x 6 (nominal) to the 1½ x 4 in. (actual) with 16d nails at 16 in. on center. End-nail the plates to the two studs with four 16d nails at each end.

Frame the wall(s) where the duct openings will be located. If the opening is near a corner of the wall, frame the closest stud a minimum of 6 in. from the double corner stud, or 12 in. from the single corner stud (Panel C, 1-B2; 4-B2). This will allow space to predrill the corner studs for the corner bolt connections, once the panels are in place. Frame the other stud for the opening at 24 in. on center to the first. Fasten a horizontal 2 x 6 (nominal) with its top edge 8 in. down from the bottom of the top plate, with two 16d common nails at each end.

Sheathing

Sheathe the walls with ½-in. CDX plywood. Begin the sheathing flush with the outside edge of the double stud, and continue across to a point 6 in. beyond the single stud (1-B2). The plywood should be 6'0" high, extending 1½ in. above the top plate (3, 4-B2). Cut out the sheathing covering the duct openings. The four edges of the plywood should fall over a stud or plate. Fasten the plywood with 8d common nails at 6 in. on center around the sheet edges, and 12 in. on center at intermediate studs.

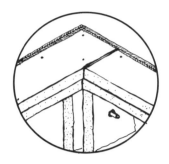

6.4 BIN ASSEMBLY

The four panels are tipped into place and bolted together. Each one is laid on a strip of sill insulation, which will help prevent heat loss through cracks between the bottom plate and the slab.

The panels are bolted together, not just toe-nailed. This will keep the walls together during the loading process, and under the constant stress of the rocks' weight for the life of the rock bin.

The R-19 fiberglass batt insulation between the studs will help keep the heat stored in the rocks.

Lay 6-in.-wide asphalt-impregnated "sill insulation" on the slab, around the perimeter of the rock bin. Force it down over the anchor bolts. Tip the first two walls into place over the sill insulation, matching a double-stud end with a single-stud end at the intersection. The 6-in. plywood extension on the outside of the single-stud end should cover the outer stud on the double-stud end (2-B3). If possible (depending on site conditions), nail the plywood to the outside double-stud. If one or both of the walls is a bolt wall, fasten the nuts over the anchor bolts.

While bracing the two walls in place, drill ½-in.-diameter holes from the single-stud side through the single-stud and the inner double-stud (2, 4-B3). The holes should be set back 3 in. from the inside face of the stud. The top and bottom holes should be 6 in. from the top and bottom of the panel, and then the rest should be spaced at 1'8" on center (4-B3). Bolt the two panels together with ½ x 4½ in. bolts with washers.

Fasten the next wall to one of those already standing, nailing the plywood extension, predrilling and bolting through the studs. Fasten the next one to it, and finally the last one to the first (from the inside). Fasten the second top plate to the first with 16d common nails, staggered at 16 in. on center (1-B3). Overlap the plates at the corners for better strength (3-B3), and face-nail with two 16d nails at each corner. Leave a 3½-in. space in the two plates over the walls that will be perpendicular to the center partition (3-B3). Center the spaces over the center-lines of the walls, over the 2 x 6 (nominal) blocking flush with the interior of the panels.

Insulate the walls with R-19 fiberglass batt the full width of the studs. Staple the paper face to the inside face of the studs. Do not insulate the duct openings.

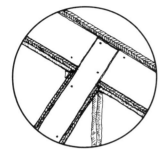

6.5 INTERIOR WALLS

The first step in this section is to assemble and add the center divider to the rock bin. The divider will keep the air from "short-circuiting" over the top of the rocks, making the air take the long route down through the rocks, under the divider, and up through the rocks on the other side.

The second step is to sheathe the inside of the rock bin. This will give the walls more structural integrity. The third step is to cover the sheathing with gypsum board. This not only protects the plywood from the heat, but it also provides a good airtight seal with its tape and joint process. The gypsum is applied perpendicularly to the plywood so that any air that does leak through a seam has a harder time reaching a seam in the plywood.

Center Divider

The center partition or divider that separates the two sides of the rock bin should be built out of 2 x 4s (nominal) at 16 in. on center. The height of the 2 x 4 panel will be 5'0½" (2-B4). The partition will be fastened to the two perpendicular walls, with the bottom of its shoe plate 10 in. from the slab. This will allow space for the rigid insulation and concrete blocks in Section 6.6 to slide underneath it. The top plate of the divider will splice into the two spaces left in the perpendicular walls top plate (1, 6-B4).

Build the center partition, end-nailing the plates to the studs with two 16d common nails at each stud. Predrill ½-in. holes through the two end studs at 1'0" on center, with the top and bottom holes no more than 4 in. from the top and bottom of the wall. Brace the divider in place inside the rock bin, matching up the bottom edge of its top plate with that of the panels' lower top plates. Center each end stud on the centerline of the 2 x 6 (nominal) blocking at the midpoints of the perpendicular walls. This will be under the spaces left in their top plates. Fasten the divider to the blocking, and into the 2 x behind it, with ½ x 4 in. lag screws (3-B4).

Fasten the double top plate to the top plate of the center divider with 16d common nails staggered at 16 in. on center, splicing it into spaces left in the top plate of the perpendicular walls (1-B4). Fasten the ends to the perpendicular walls, face-nailing with two 16d common nails at each end (6-B4).

Sheathing

Sheathe the inside of the rock bin with ½-in. CDX plywood (5-B4). Fasten with 8d common nails at 6 in. on center around the sheet edges, and 12 in. on center at the intermediate studs. Position the sheets of plywood with the long sides over the studs and the short sides over the plates. The vertical edges of the plywood must fall over a stud to help minimize air leakage and to support the plywood against the force of the rocks. Make sure the edges of the plywood butt hard against the floor, the corners, and against each other. Sheathe all the panels, as well as the center partition, from the top to the bottom plate (4-B4). Don't forget to fasten the sheathing across the bottom of the perpendicular walls, covering the 10-in-high gap between the center partition and the slab.

Run a ¼-in. continuous bead of silicone caulk around the bottom edge of the plywood, where it butts against the slab (4-B4). (See Appendix A for caulk recommendations.)

Gypsum Board

Fasten ½-in. gypsum board over the interior face of the plywood with its long sides perpendicular to the long sides of the sheathing. Fasten with 1-in. drywall screws at 8 in. on center around the edges, and 12 in. on center into every stud (where the nails are in the plywood). Stagger the gypsum board edges with the plywood edges at the interior corners (7-B4). If the plywood edge butts into another sheet of plywood, butt the gypsum into the plywood also, and then the perpendicular sheet of gypsum into the first piece of gypsum. Fasten the gypsum only to the sheathing on the panels, not to the sheathing on the center partition. Don't forget to fasten the gypsum board across the bottom of the perpendicular walls, covering the 10-in.-gap between the center partition and the slab.

Apply the base coat of joint compound over the seams in the gypsum, and embed the reinforcing tape into it. Center the tape over *all* the seams and into all the corners. Apply two coats of compound over the tape, waiting for the first coat to dry before applying the next. While waiting for each coat to dry, apply a coat to the screw heads across the face of the gypsum. Repeat until tape and screws are covered with two coats of joint compound (7-B4). The joint compound will reduce air leakage from the bin.

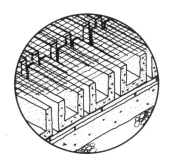

6.6 BOND BLOCK

This section deals with preparing the floor of the rock bin for the loading of the rocks. The insulation keeps the heat from flowing out through the floor slab. Since it is exposed to the air stream, any insulation that burns, or is toxic when it does, cannot be used. The insulation must also be able to withstand 3 to 4 psi under the loading of the rocks.

Insulation

Lay 2 ft. x 4 ft. x 1 in. sheets of rigid *nonflammable, nontoxic* insulation across the floor of the rock bin. Lay another 1 in. layer over the first, staggering all the edges. *Do not* lay one edge directly over any other (3, 4-B5). (See Appendix A for recommendations.)

Setting Bond Blocks

The bond blocks have a special core that directs the air flow toward and under the divider. Since the cores are open across the top of the blocks, and because there are spaces for air flow between the blocks themselves, all the blocks are covered with a layer of ¾-in. self-furring metal lath. This *must* be the type of lath used. It is the only one structurally capable of keeping out the rocks and fines that could clog the lower air plenum.

Center one row of concrete, open-ended bond-beam blocks (8 x 8 x 16 in.) under the center partition. The blocks should be placed with their open core (and 16-in. side) perpendicular to the center divider, to allow air to pass under the partition. Space the blocks from 2 in. to 4 in. apart, and 2 in. to 4 in. away from the perpendicular walls. The actual distance will depend on the actual interior width of the box (1, 3-B5).

Using the centered row of blocks as a guide, place the blocks end-to-end across the whole floor of the rock bed, with their long sides parallel to the perpendicular walls. Space the sides again at 2 in. to 4 in. apart, and away from the walls. Space them also 2 in. to 4 in. apart in the long direction, and away from the walls (4-B5). The actual spacing will depend on the actual interior dimension of the rock bin.

Metal Lath

Beginning at the end of the box, lay ¾-in. self-furring metal lath across the block, with its long edge perpendicular to the block. (See Appendix A for lath recommendations.) Cut it 1'0" longer than the interior width of the box. Bend the three edges up the three walls. Overlap the next layer 6 in. over the first. Cut and bend the sheet up the two side walls. Continue until the last sheet bends a minimum of 6 in. up the divider (1, 3, 4-B5).

Repeat for the other side of the rock bin, overlapping all the layers 6 in., and bending a minimum of 6 in. up the walls (1-B5).

Duct Collars

Have two duct collars fabricated out of 30-gauge sheet metal. The collars will have 1½-in. nailing flanges around one end. The collars will be 8 in. high, 22½ in. wide, and 9 in. from back to front (2-B5).

Caulk around the perimeter of the duct collar openings on the gypsum board (inside the bin) with a ¼-in. continuous bead of silicone caulk. Insert the duct collars from the *inside* of the bin, pushing the nailing flanges into the caulk. Fasten around the nailing flanges with 1½-in. drywall screws at 4 in. on center (2-B5).

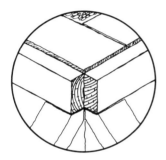

6.7 BRACING AND LOADING

The rock bin must be prepared for the loading of the rocks by bracing the walls. The braces must remain in place until the cover of the rock bin is *completely* fastened in place. The cover will then take over the job of keeping the tops of the walls from spreading apart.

The rocks must be tested and cleaned before they are loaded into the bin. Both these steps are important to performance. The correct amount of void between the rocks, determined in the test, is essential for proper air flow. And if the rocks go into the bin covered with dirt, the dirt could fall down between the rocks and plug the holes in the metal lath. This could cut off the air flow from one side of the bin to the other.

Bracing

All bolt walls must be braced against the impact and sustained load of the rock until the lid is securely bolted in place. The braces are 2 x 4 (nominal) lengths, which run at a 45° angle from a 2 x 4 (nominal) "ledger" nailed to the top of the bin walls, to a 2 x 4 (nominal) "shear plate" shot into the slab.

Nail continuous 2 x 4 ledgers to the sides of the bolt walls, with their top 1½-in. faces flush with the top of the walls. Fasten temporarily with double-headed 16d nails staggered at 16 in. on center. Stay within 1 in. of the centerline of the 3½ in. face when nailing, or the nails may miss the top plates (1, 2-B6).

Lay the 2 x 4 shear plates on the slab, with the outside 1½-in. side 6'0" away from the side of the bin. Shoot into the concrete with ¼ x 3⁷/₁₆ in. powder-driven pins at 24 in. on center (1, 2-B6).

Cut 2 x 4 braces that will span from the ledger to the shear plate. Beginning at one corner of the bin, wedge one end of the brace under the ledger, bow the 2 x 4 down, and butt the other end against the inside edge of the shear plate. Work across the side, spacing the braces at 2'0" on center. Place one brace flush with the other corner. Repeat this process for all bolt walls (1, 2-B6).

Do not remove the braces until the cover to the rock bin has been fastened in place.

Preparation and Loading

ROCKS. The rock that will be used in the bin should be a mixture of ¾ to 1½ in. crushed rock. To get this mixture, have the plant screen the rock twice: once through a 1½-in. screen to filter out any rocks bigger than 1½ in. in diameter, and once through a ¾-in. screen to filter out any rocks smaller than ¾ inch. This mixture of rock should give the correct ratio of solids to voids, and the correct amount of surface area. Both are needed for good heat transfer, from the air to the rocks (storage), or the rocks to the air (delivery). The mixture should be washed at least once, and preferably twice, before leaving the plant.

VOID TEST. *Before* purchasing the rock, a void test of the mixture should be run. The mixture must be graded to contain no less than 40% voids around the rocks, or the air will not be able to pass by the rocks at the proper rate. If the air goes by the rocks too slowly or too quickly, the heat transfer in the storage or the delivery modes is not the rate upon which the size of the rock bin was based.

Fill a 55-gallon drum with the rock sample. Pour measured quantities of water into the drum, one gallon at a time. Keep track of the number of gallons the drum receives, until it overflows. If the drum holds between 22 and 27½ gallons of water, the sample passes the test.

CLEANING AND LOADING. Have the rock delivered to the site and dumped near the building onto a sheet of 6-mil polyethylene. The plastic will help keep the rocks clean. *Do not* have the truck dump the rocks into the box.

FIG. 6.4 TESTING THE PERCENTAGE OF VOID IN ROCK

Hose down the rocks, forcing the fines and small pieces of debris to the bottom of the pile. Let the rocks dry before loading them into the bin.

Note: It is easier to load the rock and fasten the lid if the first-floor framing is not yet in place.

Load the rocks into the bin, filling each side equally during loading to minimize strain on the divider. Place the rock slowly, in small loads, to minimize stress on the metal lath, blocks, and bin interior. Fill the bin to a point 4′0″ from the floor slab. Place

FIG. 6.5 ROCK AT THE SITE, READY TO BE WASHED AND LOADED

the temperature sensor piping in the bin, then fill the rest of the
bin to a point 12 in. from the top of the walls (1-B6). *Do not* use
the rocks from the bottom of the pile. Any fines or debris could
work their way down through the rocks and could plug the holes
in the metal lath.

Temperature Sensors

Two temperature sensors should be placed in the rock bin, one on each side of the divider. (See Appendix A for recommendations.) The sensor that came with the differential controller will be placed in the cold side of storage, and the sensor attached to the remote bulb thermostat will be placed in the hot side. *Remember*, the hot side of storage is the side connected to the return duct of the collector, and the cold side is the side connected to the supply duct.

Drill two ½-in.-diameter holes 1'0" away from the duct collars (5-B6), and 4'0" from the floor slab (6-B6). Cut two 3-ft.-long sections of ½-in.-outside-diameter iron pipe and thread one end of each. Feed the pipes through the holes until 2 in. are left on the outside of the bin. Caulk continuously with silicone around each pipe where it intersects the gypsum board (3-B6).

Apply silicone caulk around the pipes where they intersect the exterior plywood. Place pipe collars over the pipes, caulk around their edges, and fasten them to the rock bin (3-B6). Load the rocks gently over the pipes.

Feed the sensors, with the wires connected, into the pipes, until they meet resistance at the end of the pipe. Feed the wires through holes in the end of ½-in.-diameter pipe caps, and fasten the caps to the pipes. Caulk the holes in the caps (3-B6).

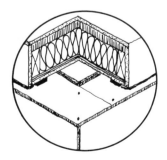

6.8 COVER ASSEMBLY

The cover serves two functions. One is to keep the heat from flowing out the top of the rock bin, so it is insulated with both fiberglass batt and extruded polystyrene. The cover also has to keep the tops of the bin walls from spreading under the load of the rocks within, so the number of bolts specified is very important.

The seam between the cover and the top of the walls *must* be airtight. That is why the process includes a neoprene gasket plus a seal of silicone caulk *all the way around* the perimeter.

The seal across the top of the center divider is also important. It must be airtight to keep air from short-circuiting from one side to the other. This is why two gaskets instead of one are used, with a space left between them where the lag screws can pass by without disturbing them.

Framing

The frame for the cover will be 4 in. smaller in width and length than the width and length of the rock bin walls. Frame the cover with 2 x 4s (nominal) at 24 in. on center, as if it were a wall being framed, with its 2 x 4s parallel with the center divider. Frame one 2 x 4 with its centerline along the centerline of the cover. End-nail each "plate" into the studs with two 16d common nails at each end of the studs (3-B7).

Interior Finish

Sheathe the inside of the cover with ½-in. CDX plywood (2-B7). Fasten with 8d common nails at 6 in. on center around the sheet edges, and 12 in. on center at the intermediate 2 x 4s. Position the sheets of plywood with their long sides over the 2 x 4s, and the short sides over the perimeter frame. The edges of the plywood must fall over the framing to help minimize air leakage and to support the plywood. Carry the sheathing to the outer edges of the perimeter framing members (2-B7).

Fasten ½-in. gypsum board over the interior face of the plywood with its long sides perpendicular to the long sides of the sheathing. Fasten with 1-in. drywall screws at 8 in. on center around the edges, and 12 in. on center into every stud (where the nails are in the plywood). Sink each screw just below the surface, to be covered with joint compound later (2-B7). Carry the gypsum to the outer edges of the perimeter framing members (2-B7).

Apply the base coat of joint compound over the seams in the gypsum, and embed the reinforcing tape into it. Center the tape over *all* the seams. Apply two coats of compound over the tape, waiting for the first coat to dry before applying the next. While waiting for each coat to dry, apply a coat to the screw heads across the face of the gypsum. Repeat until tape and screws are covered with two coats of joint compound (2-B7). The joint compound will reduce air leakage from the bin.

Insulation

Insulate between the framing members with 3½ in. of fiberglass batt. Sheathe over the top of the members with 4 x 8 sheets of tongue-and-groove rigid extruded polystyrene insulation. (See Appendix A for extruded polystyrene recommendations.) The edges of the sheets should all be supported by the framing members. Fasten the polystyrene with 1½-in. nails with 7/16-in. heads, at 12 in. on center around the edges and over the framing members. Carry the sheathing to the outer edges of the perimeter framing members (2-B7).

Exterior Finish

Cover the top and side faces of the rock bin cover with ½-in. gypsum board, with its long sides perpendicular to the long sides of the polystyrene (2-B7). Fasten with 2-in. drywall screws at 8 in. on center, and 12 in. on center into every framing member (note the nails in the polystyrene).

Cover the four sides of the cover first, from the bottom edge of the gypsum on the bottom (interior) face of the cover, to the top of the polystyrene insulation. Then cover the top of the cover, lapping the perimeter edges over the top of the side gypsum (2-B7).

Apply the base coat of joint compound over the seams in the gypsum, and over the edges of the cover (start with the top corners). Center the tape over all the seams and over the top four corners/edges of the cover. Apply two coats of compound over the tape, waiting for each coat to dry before applying the next. While waiting for each coat to dry, apply a coat to the screw heads across the faces of the gypsum. Repeat until the tape and screws are covered with two coats of joint compound (2-B7).

Turn the cover over, and repeat the process for the bottom four corners/edges of the cover (2-B7).

Predrill holes for the ½ x 8 in. lag screws. The ⅜-in.-diameter holes should be drilled around the perimeter of the cover, at 2'0" on center. The centerline of the holes should be set 1¼ in. back from the side edges of the cover. Also predrill the holes at 2'0" along the centerline of the cover (that will be directly over the divider of the rock bin). These screws will run down through the

2 x 4 at the centerline of the cover, and into the top plate of the divider.

Neoprene Gaskets

Run a ¼-in. continuous bead of silicone caulk around the top of the perimeter walls, 4 in. back from the exterior face of the rock bin exterior sheathing. Lay a continuous line of ½ x 2 in. closed-cell neoprene gasket over the caulk, with its interior ½-in. face set 5 in. back from the exterior face of the rock bin exterior sheathing (2-B7). (See Appendix A for silicone caulk and neoprene gasket recommendations. *Do not* use polyvinylchloride foam tape, but *closed-cell* neoprene. Check with the manufacturer to be sure their neoprene can be used with silicone caulk, because some kinds cannot.)

Run two continuous ¼-in. beads of caulk across the top plate of the divider wall, each set 1 in. inside the exterior edge of the plywood. Lay one continuous gasket over each line of caulk, with its exterior edge lined up with the exterior face of the plywood (2-B7). Let the caulk set before laying the rock bin cover over the gaskets.

Cover Fastening

Lay the cover in place on top of the gaskets, with its side edges 1½ in. inside the exterior face of the sheathing on the walls (2-B7). *Do not* slide the cover across the gasket, but *set in place*. Fasten the cover in place with ½ x 8 in. lag screws, through the predrilled holes around the perimeter and across the centerline. *Fill* the gap left around the bin perimeter, between the gypsum, gasket and top plate with caulk.

   RETROFIT: It may be awkward, but it is necessary that someone crawl over the top of the cover and caulk any seams that can't be reached otherwise.

Remove the temporary bracing, shear plate, and ledger *after* all the lag screws have been fastened. The ducts may now be attached to the duct collars and the rock bin connected to the air-handling system, collector, and controls.

CHAPTER 7

MODEL-TEA SYSTEM CONTROL WIRING

181

The collector captures sunlight and converts it to heat, the air-handling system delivers that heat to the proper place, and the rock bin stores surplus heat for later use. But the electrical control system is the vital link which enables the three parts to work together.

Chapters 4 and 5 give step-by-step instructions for constructing the MODEL-TEA roof or wall collector, and Chapter 6 gives detailed instructions for building the rock bin. This chapter presents the control wiring for the entire system.

Because the air-handling arrangement is particularly site and system dependent, step-by-step instructions are not given. However, Sections 1.3, 2.3, and 3.4 contain all the necessary information on the air-handling components and their relationships within a system. Tables 3.1, 3.2 and 3.3 supply data on the components that should be ordered for a given size system. An alternative to site building the air-handling system from components is to buy a commercially manufactured prepackaged unit. This option is discussed in Section 8.1.

The information supplied in Chapters 2 and 3 should be read by an experienced heating contractor in planning the system. Not enough information is supplied here to enable the inexperienced layman to do the work. The ductwork layout is site dependent, and its arrangement has many effects on the air-handling system.

The air-handling work should be subcontracted to a skilled heating contractor who can properly plan and install this system. Early in the planning stages, advice should be obtained on placement of duct runs and ordering of components. The same person who installs the ductwork should have access to the equipment to prefabricate the manifold pans and collars, and the backdraft and slide dampers. The return and supply ductwork should be connected to the collector prior to the smoke test (Sections 4.8 and 5.8) so that they, too, can be tested for leaks. After the test, the remainder of the ductwork, the blowers, motors, dampers, and filter can be installed. Once all the connections between the air-handling equipment and the ductwork are complete, the control wiring can begin.

Control wiring information is presented with sufficiently detailed schematics so that an electrical engineer or skilled mechanical contractor familiar with control systems can wire the controls. This information would be inadequate for the layman, and might not be sufficient for an electrician.

This chapter is subdivided into four parts. The first is a description of the various system options available, with a table that will direct the installer to the correct diagrams. The second section is a description of the modes of operation, providing information on the signaling of the various modes. The third section presents a "ladder diagram," or wiring schematic, for each of the options that incorporate remote storage. These schematics are useful for understanding the details of the control system. Section three continues with a discussion of the field wiring diagrams and the control panel wiring. Section four discusses those systems without storage, and includes wiring schematics and field and control wiring.

An alternative to wiring the system on site is to buy a prepackaged control unit. There are commercially manufactured units available on the market, but they will not perform exactly the same as the system presented in this chapter. Many firms will modify their units to specifications, but this will add to the cost of the unit. It could be less expensive in the long run to buy a prepackaged air-handling system that is supplied with its own controls.

Once the control wiring is finished, the system is ready to be started up and tested through all the modes. Make sure that the contract with the professional doing the wiring includes this process, as well as fixing any problems that might be encountered.

7.1 SYSTEM OPTIONS

Table 7.1 shows the different options available when planning the MODEL-TEA system. Running through the choices of roof or wall collector, remote storage or direct daytime heating, and DHW or no DHW leads the reader to the appropriate wiring diagrams that should be followed when wiring that particular system.

There are many site, performance, economic, and personal criteria affecting the final choices made. For example, if a roof collector is chosen over the wall collector, an investment in

TABLE 7.1
MODEL-TEA SYSTEM OPTIONS

Retrofit (Parallel Auxiliary); see Fig. 7.2

I. Wall Collector
    A. With Storage
        1. Without DHW
            See Figs. 7.13, 7.17, 7.22, 7.29
        2. With DHW
            See Figs. 7.14, 7.18, 7.22, 7.24, 7.29
    B. Without Storage
        1. Without DHW
            See Figs. 7.25, 7.27, 7.29
II. Roof Collector
    A. With Storage
        1. Without DHW
            See Figs. 7.15, 7.19, 7.22, 7.23, 7.29
        2. With DHW
            See Figs. 7.16, 7.20, 7.22, 7.23, 7.24, 7.29
    B. Without Storage
        1. With DHW
            See Figs. 7.26, 7.27, 7.28, 7.29
        2. Without DHW
            See Figs. 7.26, 7.28, 7.29

New Construction (Series Auxiliary); see Fig. 7.1

I. Wall Collector
    A. With Storage
        1. Without DHW
            See Figs. 7.9, 7.17, 7.21, 7.29
        2. With DHW
            See Figs. 7.10, 7.18, 7.21, 7.24, 7.29
    B. Without Storage
        1. Without DHW
            See Figs. 7.25, 7.28, 7.29
II. Roof Collector
    A. With Storage
        1. Without DHW
            See Figs. 7.11, 7.19, 7.21, 7.23, 7.29
        2. With DHW
            See Figs. 7.12, 7.20, 7.21, 7.23, 7.24, 7.29

TABLE 7.1, continued
MODEL-TEA SYSTEM OPTIONS

New Construction (Series Auxiliary); see Fig. 7.1, continued

   B. Without Storage
      1. With DHW
         See Figs. 7.26, 7.27, 7.28, 7.29
      2. Without DHW
         See Figs. 7.26, 7.28, 7.29

power-venting equipment must be made. This includes two additional sensors in the collector with their attendant overheating alarm circuits, one additional switch, and two manually operated slide dampers, each with two separate housings and two interchangeable blades. Also required are two duct runs to the outside, through grilles with removable insulation and filters.

If the collector is large enough (greater than 150–200 square feet) to cause overheating of the living space, then a remote-storage rock bin must be constructed. This choice involves not just the cost of the rock bin, but the extra ductwork to carry the heat to it, an additional fan to retrieve the heat, two to three additional motorized dampers to direct the air, one extra back-draft damper, one differential controller (with one sensor on the collector and one sensor in storage), and one additional sensor in the rock bin, with added cost for the control circuit.

Another decision is whether or not to include DHW. With a large roof collector, the only reason not to use it is if there is an existing DHW system. The only time DHW should be included with a wall collector is if the collecter is large enough to make the option cost-effective. A decision to include the DHW mode will add the cost of another differential controller (with a sensor in the collector, and one on the preheat DHW tank), one extra switch and one extra relay, a 60 to 80 gallon preheat tank, a circulating pump, a heat exchanger to go in the ductwork, and miscellaneous piping, valves and flanges. With a wall collector, it would also mean the addition of one pair of slide dampers and extra ductwork.

The addition of these costs should be considered each time a choice is made. If the cost of the DHW mode seems out of the question now, the additional sensor could be included in the collector during construction and the wires run to the control panel. The DHW system could then be added later, without taking the collector apart to add the sensor.

7.2 MODES OF OPERATION

Before beginning work on the control wiring, it is important to understand the operation of the modes. There is one basic mode common to systems with or without storage, and that is "collector to house." This is the only mode available on a wall collector system with no storage. The systems with storage share two additional modes: "collector to storage" and "storage

MODE	M.D.1	M.D.2	M.D.3	C.FAN	H.FAN	B.D.1	B.D.2	DHW	S.D.1	S.D.2	AUX.	SIGNALS
							WINTER					
COLLECTOR TO HOUSE	O	O	C	ON	ON	O	O	OFF	W.P.	W.P.	OFF	ΔT, W_1
											ON	AT, W_1, W_2
COLLECTOR TO STORAGE	O	C	O	ON	OFF	O	C	OFF	W.P.	W.P.	OFF	ΔT
								ON				AT, AT_{HW}
STORAGE TO HOUSE	C	O	O	OFF	ON	C	O	OFF	W.P.	W.P.	OFF	W_1, $RB_T > 85°F$
											ON	W_1, W_2 OR
											ON	W_1, $RB_T < 85°F$, W_2
							SUMMER					
POWER VENT	O	C	–	ON	OFF	–	–	–	S.P.	S.P.	OFF	$T_{COL} > 180°F$
D H W	O	C	–	ON	OFF	–	–	ON	S.P.	S.P.	OFF	AT_{HW} OR $T_{COL} > 180°F$

FIG. 7.1 MODE SCHEDULE FOR NEW CONSTRUCTION

KEY

O	OPEN	C	CLOSED
M.D.	MOTORIZED DAMPER	C.FAN	COLLECTOR FAN
M.D.1	COLLECTOR	H.FAN	HOUSE FAN
M.D.2	HOUSE	D.H.W.	DOMESTIC HOT WATER
M.D.3	STORAGE	AT	20°F AT COLL./STOR.
B.D.	BACKDRAFT DAMPER	W_1	1ST CALL FOR HEAT
S.D.	SLIDE DAMPER	W_2	2ND CALL FOR HEAT
S.D.1	POWER VENT EXHAUST	RB_T	ROCK BIN TEMPERATURE
S.D.2	POWER VENT INTAKE	AT_{HW}	40°F AT PRE-HEAT TANK/COLL.
AUX	AUXILIARY HEATING	T_{COL}	TEMPERATURE OF COLLECTOR
W.P.	WINTER POSITION	S.P.	SUMMER POSITION

to house." Roof collectors must have the mode called "power venting," whether they have remote storage or not. Adding DHW to the system adds the "domestic hot water" mode, and in the summer this combines with the "power venting" mode for the roof collector, resulting in the "DHW and power vent mode." In all, there are six different possibilities.

There are three parts to a mode. The signals, or inputs, are sent to the system. The controls interpret these signals as a certain mode, and then in turn send their own signals, or outputs, to different parts of the system to make that mode happen.

There are two mode schedules to follow, found in Figures 7.1 and 7.2. One is for retrofit and one is for new construction. The only difference between a new construction system and a retrofit system is that the auxiliary heating system is in parallel with the solar air-handling system in retrofit, and in series in new construction.

FIG. 7.2 MODE SCHEDULE FOR RETROFIT											
MODE	M.D.1	M.D.2	M.D.3	C.FAN	H.FAN	B.D.1	B.D.2	DHW	S.D.1	S.D.2	AUX.	SIGNALS
WINTER											
COLLECTOR TO HOUSE	O	O	C	ON	ON	O	O	OFF	W.P.	W.P.	OFF	$\Delta T, W_1$
											ON	$\Delta T, W_1, W_2, RB_T > 85°F$
COLLECTOR TO STORAGE	O	C	O	ON.	OFF	O	C	OFF	W.P.	W.P.	OFF	ΔT
								ON				$\Delta T, \Delta T_{HW}$
								-			ON	W_2
STORAGE TO HOUSE	C	O	O	OFF	ON	C	O	OFF	W.P.	W.P.	OFF	$W_1, RB_T > 85°F$
											ON	$W_1, W_2, RB_T > 85°F$
AUXILIARY ONLY	C	O	-	OFF	OFF	C	C	OFF	W.P.	W.P.	ON	$W_1, W_2, RB_T < 85°F$
SUMMER											
POWER VENT	O	C	-	ON	OFF	-	-	-	S.P.	S.P.	OFF	$T_{COL} > 180°F$
D.H.W	O	C	-	ON	OFF	-	-	ON	S.P.	S.P.	OFF	ΔT_{HW} OR $T_{COL} > 180°F$

KEY

O	OPEN		C	CLOSED	
M.D.	MOTORIZED DAMPER		C.FAN	COLLECTOR FAN	
M.D.1	COLLECTOR		H.FAN	HOUSE FAN	
M.D.2	HOUSE		D.H.W.	DOMESTIC HOT WATER COIL	
M.D.3	STORAGE		ΔT	20°F ΔT COLL./STOR.	
B.D.	BACKDRAFT DAMPER		W_1	1ST CALL FOR HEAT	
S.D.	SLIDE DAMPER		W_2	2ND CALL FOR HEAT	
S.D.1	POWER VENT EXHAUST		RB_T	ROCK BIN TEMPERATURE	
S.D.2	POWER VENT INTAKE		ΔT_{HW}	40°F ΔT PRE-HEAT TANK/COLL.	
AUX.	AUXILIARY HEATING		T_{COL}	TEMPERATURE OF COLLECTOR	
W.P.	WINTER POSITION		S.P.	SUMMER POSITION	

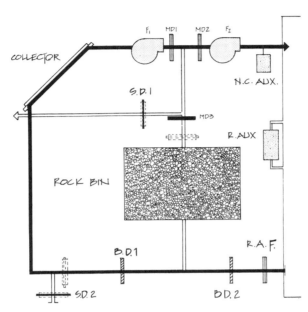

FIG. 7.3 COLLECTOR-TO-HOUSE MODE

LEGEND	
C. FAN	COLLECTOR FAN
H. FAN	HOUSE FAN
N.C. AUX.	NEW CONSTRUCTION AUXILIARY POSITION
R. AUX	RETROFIT AUXILIARY POSITION
D.H.W.C	DOMESTIC HOT WATER COIL
S.D.	SLIDE DAMPER WITH TWO POSITIONS
B.D.	BACKDRAFT DAMPER
R.A.F.	RETURN AIR FILTER
M.D.	MOTORIZED DAMPER

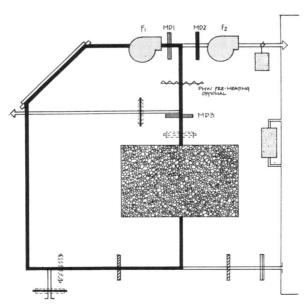

FIG. 7.4 COLLECTOR-TO-STORAGE MODE

The Six Modes

COLLECTOR TO HOUSE (FIGURE 7.3). Whenever there is a first-stage call for heat by the house (W_1), and the collectors are at least 20°F hotter than the storage (ΔT), hot air is drawn directly from the collectors. Motorized dampers 1 and 2 (M.D. 1 and M.D. 2) open and motorized damper 3 (M.D. 3) remains closed. Both the collector fan (F_1) and the house fan (F_2) turn on. Heat is drawn from the collectors and blown into the house, with cool room air being sent to the collector. This is a priority mode and will occur whenever there is a call for heat and the collectors are hot enough to supply it.

COLLECTOR TO STORAGE (FIGURE 7.4). Whenever the collectors are at least 20°F hotter than storage (ΔT), and this heat is not needed by the house (W_1) the heat is stored in the rock bin. In this mode, M.D. 1 and M.D. 3 open and the collector fan (F_1) turns on. Since M.D. 2 is closed, the hot air is forced through the rock bin, transferring its heat to the rocks. Cool air is then returned to the collector.

STORAGE TO HOUSE (FIGURE 7.5). This mode occurs whenever there is heat in storage ($RB_T > 85°F$) and the house calls for heat (W_1), but there isn't enough heat in the collectors (ΔT). In this case, M.D.2 and M.D.3 open and the house fan (F_2) comes on, drawing hot air from the storage and delivering it to the house. Cool room air is drawn through the rocks to be heated.

The auxiliary system will come on any time there is a second-stage call for heat (W_2), which happens when the house temperature drops approximately 2°F below stage one (W_1). This can happen if there is not sufficient heat in the collectors (ΔT) or in the storage ($RB_T < 85°F$). But it can also happen if, in a very cold spell, the heat delivered from storage is not by itself sufficient to balance the heat loss.

In retrofit systems, the second-stage call for heat (W_2) turns on the parallel auxiliary, independent of what is happening in the solar air-handling system. If there is not enough heat in the collectors (ΔT) or storage ($RB_T < 85°F$), the dampers close and the fans shut off. But if there is heat in storage ($RB_T > 85°F$), the

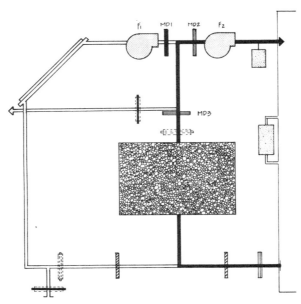

FIG. 7.5 STORAGE-TO-HOUSE MODE

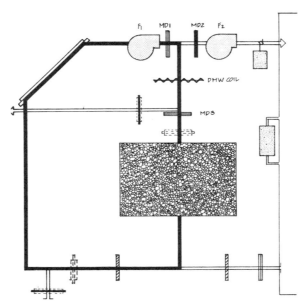

FIG. 7.6 DHW MODE

---

storage-to-house mode will continue supplying heat to the house at the same time as the auxiliary heating system.

In new construction systems, the second-stage call for heat (W_2) turns on the series auxiliary. The auxiliary boosts the temperature of the already preheated air coming from the collectors or storage.

DOMESTIC HOT WATER (FIGURE 7.6). DHW operation occurs when the collector temperature reaches a point 40°F higher than the water in the preheat tank (ΔT_{HW}), and the system is either storing heat or venting it (power venting). The pump turns on to circulate the water from the preheat tank through the heat exchanger coil that is located in the hot air duct. The water in the coil picks up the heat from the hot air drawn down from the collector.

POWER VENTING (FIGURE 7.7). The power venting mode is only used with the roof collector, to cool the collector in the summer and extend the life of the collector materials. This mode requires the homeowner to throw a switch and move the two slide dampers from winter to summer positions in the spring, and back to the winter positions in the fall. The switch will be located on the control board and, when thrown to the summer position, will activate the extra sensor in the collector. The slide dampers, when in the summer position, connect the collector supply and return ducts to the outside. When the temperature of the collector exceeds 180°F (T_{COL}), the sensor in the collector closes, and the collector-to-storage mode is activated. But with the slide dampers in their summer positions, the hot air from the collector bypasses the rock bin and is vented outside. Air from the outside is returned to the collector.

DHW AND POWER VENTING (FIGURE 7.8). In the summer, the domestic hot water mode can operate either in its normal mode (ΔT_{HW}), or it may operate during power venting, when the roof collector temperature exceeds 180°F (T_{COL}). When the collector power vents, the pump circulates the water from the preheat tank through the heat exchanger coil in the duct, recovering some of the heat from the air before it is exhausted to the outside.

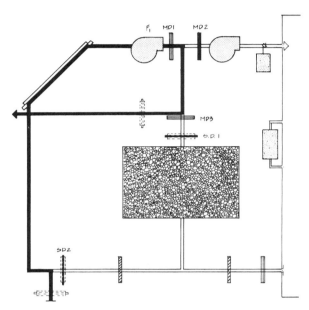

FIG. 7.7 POWER VENTING MODE

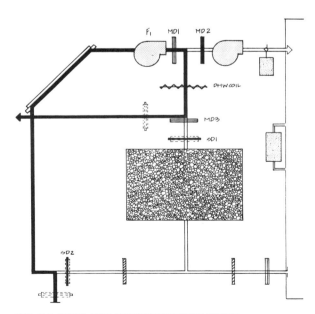

FIG. 7.8 DHW AND POWER VENTING MODE

Summer vs. Winter Operation

When spring arrives, the system must be changed from its winter to its summer operation. Whether it is a roof or a wall collector, the first step is to disconnect the differential controller between collector and storage. This will keep the system from operating whenever ΔT occurs, which would result in overheating the rock bin and/or the house. In systems with power venting and/or DHW, the slide dampers must be moved from their winter to their summer positions. In addition, switch S must be flicked from its winter to summer position. This will activate T_{COL}, and will convert the winter heating system to the summer DHW and/or power venting system.

Exactly when in the spring this process should occur is up to the individual. Once the differential controller is shut off or disconnected, solar heating is no longer available to the house, and the auxiliary heating system must carry the load alone. The earlier in the spring this is done, the greater the chance that the house will call for heat and the auxiliary will have to respond. Some individuals might combine disconnecting the differential with turning down the thermostat, and then be willing to endure lower temperatures to save energy. Other individuals might wait until later in the season to switch over, often storing more heat than will be needed. This will result in eventual overheating of the rock bin and the house—a "last resort" reminder that the collector may be in a stagnation condition.

In the fall, the process must be reversed. The differential controller must be connected, and the *switch and slide dampers* returned to their winter positions. The later this is done in the season, the more the auxiliary heating system will have to answer the call for heat.

Overheating Alarms

If the system is not changed from the winter to the summer mode, the collector will eventually overheat. To protect against damage to the collector materials, the overheating sensor, (T_{HL_1}) will trigger the alarm system (B_1) when the collector temperature reaches 200°F, indicating that the power-venting mode is not operating (see Fig. 7.29). When the collector temperature drops below 196°F, the alarm will shut off.

If nothing is done to alleviate the overheating problem, the temperature of the collector will continue to rise. In the case of the roof collector, when the temperature reaches 210°F, the second overheating sensor (T_{HL_2}) will trigger a second alarm (B_2).

Both alarms are equipped with a switch to turn them off. They are provided only for short-term relief, while arrangements are being made to repair the problem. The second alarm is provided on the roof collector as a reminder, in case the first alarm is disconnected and the problem overlooked.

The alarms not only warn of summer overheating problems, but will also warn of system malfunction if the system fails to operate properly during the normal heating season. This is why the alarms are wired separately from the system controls, and from each other. Any problem with each of the three will not electrically affect the others.

7.3 WIRING

Air-Handling System

The wiring for the MODEL-TEA air-handling system has been designed so that all the relays, switches, and damper motors can be wired with low voltage (24v AC) wiring. Only the blowers and the pump have to be wired for high voltage. This means extra savings in time and cost. In this section, there are eight different wiring schematics, or ladder diagrams: four are for the options available to retrofit systems with storage, and four are for the new construction system options with storage. The options for systems without storage are discussed in Section 7.4. The air-handling and control components and manufacturers are listed in Table 7.2.

The wiring diagrams shown in Figures 7.9 through 7.12 are for new construction, and those in Figures 7.13 through 7.16 are for retrofit. Comparing any two analagous diagrams (e.g. 7.9 and 7.13, "wall collector with storage"), it can be seen that the only difference between them involves the control relay for the auxiliary heating system (CR_{Aux}). The relay in the retrofit wiring schematic (bottom line) is a single-pole, double-throw (SPDT) relay. But in the new construction wiring schematic, the CR_{Aux} is a double-pole, double-throw (DPDT) relay, with the second contact located in parallel with RB_T. Except for putting the auxiliary heating in series with the solar system, the rest of the comparable wiring schematics are the same. Take Fig. 7.9 as an example: let us assume that the collector is 20° hotter than storage (ΔT). ΔT would close, allowing power to flow to CR_{F1} (turning on the collector fan), and to M.D.1 (opening motorized damper no. 1). Since CR_{F1} is activated, M.D.3 is powered through the CR_{F1} and CR_{W1} contacts. Since M.D.1 is powered, its micro-switch R-W contacts open, and M.D.2 remains closed. This is the collector-to-storage mode.

If there is a first-stage call for heat, W_1 closes and powers CR_{W1}. M.D.3 is deactivated, because the normally closed CR_{W1} contact opens. M.D.2 and CR_{F2} are activated through the CR_{F1} and CR_{F2} contacts, opening motorized damper 2 and turning on the House Fan. This is the collector-to-house mode.

When there is no longer any heat in the collectors, ΔT opens. But suppose there is still a first-stage call for heat and there is heat in storage. RB_T would be closed, and with W_1 already closed, CR_{F2} and M.D.2 would be activated through CR_{F1} and CR_{W1} contacts, and M.D.3 through the normally closed R-W micro-switch. Dampers 2 and 3 would open, the house fan would turn on, and the storage-to-house mode would begin.

But what if the house draws from storage until the rock bin temperature on the hot side drops below 85°F? RB_T would open, and the system would shut down. But if the house still needs heat and the first stage is not being satisfied, the second-stage calls for heat. W_2 closes, powering the auxiliary control relay (CR_{Aux}). W_1 is still closed, powering its control relays. The storage-to-house mode continues, with warm preheated air from storage being boosted by the auxiliary.

Field Wiring

The field wiring diagrams, Figures 7.17 through 7.20, show the wiring from the different parts of the system all coming together at a box called *controls*. This is the first step in actually wiring the system.

The wires to the left of the control box are all Class II (low voltage) #18 A.W.G. control or thermostat wires. However, some sensors may require shielded wire, so check the manufacturer's specifications for the sensor, or consult a control specialist. The wires to the right of the control box are Class I (115v AC) #14 A.W.G. minimum, and must be installed according to the National Electrical Code. All the wires are brought together in one central location, the control panel, to make the subsequent control steps easier.

The appropriate field wiring diagram for the system being installed should be chosen from Table 7.1. The proper sensor wires should be connected to the differential controllers, and the differential controller wires should be run to the panel. The other wires from the sensors, thermostats, dampers, fans and auxiliary should also be run to the panel, as shown in the diagrams.

Control Wiring

Wiring the control panel is split into steps. First there are two basic control wiring diagrams: one for new construction (Figure 7.21) and one for Retrofit (Figure 7.22). Each diagram can be used for either a wall or a roof collector.

Step two for the roof collector is for power venting, shown in Figure 7.23. The additional switches should be connected to the extra temperature sensor wires from the collector, and to the control relay for the house fan. The wire to the normally open CR_{F1} contact should be eliminated. Step three is the wiring of the overheating alarms, shown in Fig. 7.29.

The last step is optional: it is the control wiring for the domestic hot water, as shown in Figure 7.24. The additional switch contact should be wired to the differential controller for the domestic hot water and to the pump relay. Note that the wire to the normally open CR_{F1} contact should be eliminated.

The system should now be taken through all its modes. If there is any trouble in operation, the wiring diagrams and the connections should be rechecked.

7.4 DAYTIME SYSTEMS

The daytime systems are those systems connected directly to the living space without remote storage.

Wall Collector

In its most basic form, this system is a simple, one-mode operation. If the collector is hotter than the house and the house is not *too* hot, the collector heat is blown into the house. This type of system is well suited to retrofit, or even new construction situations, where it is impossible to have remote storage or install a large collector. Because there is no heat storage, there is a definite limitation on how large the collector can be before a significant amount of surplus heat is wasted.

The air-handling and control parts for this one-mode system are few: a collector sensor, house thermostat, fan, and backdraft damper. Figure 7.25 shows the system schematic, wiring schematic, and control wiring for the system. The components of the system and the manufacturers are called out in Table 7.2. An additional manual slide damper and extra ductwork could be added to the system to divert the hot air from the living space when it begins to overheat—perhaps sending it to a basement utility space, an inexpensive way to store heat.

Roof Collector

The roof collector daytime system expands upon the basic system by adding power venting. This principle is exactly the same as in the roof collector systems with storage. In the spring, the homeowner turns the switch that activates the extra temperature sensor in the collector, and moves the slide damper from the winter to the summer position. In this case, all that is added to the system is one switch, and one pair of slide dampers. Figure 7.26 shows the system schematic, wiring schematic, and control wiring for the system. Figure 7.27 shows the system schematic, wiring schematic, and control wiring for a roof collector with power venting and DHW. The system components and the manufacturers are listed in Table 7.2.

TABLE 7.2
AIR-HANDLING CONTROL MATERIALS

Symbol	Description	Manufacturer	Manufacturer Number
T_1	Transformer, 120 V to 24 V	Electrical Supply	—
T_2	Transformer, match voltage to buzzer (B_1) voltage	Electrical Supply	—
TGS	Toggle switch or disconnect fuse	Electrical Supply	—
F_1	Fuse	Electrical Supply	—
S_1	3PDT switch	Electrical Supply	—
CR_{F1}	3PDT relay-collector fan	Magnecraft	Class 388, 93 or 199
CR_{F2}	DPDT relay-house fan	Magnecraft	Class 388, 93 or 199
CR_p	SPDT relay-pump	Magnecraft	Class 388, 93 or 199
CR_{W1}	3PDT relay	Magnecraft	Class 388 or 78
CR_{Aux}	DPDT relay (new construction) SPDT relay (retrofit)	Magnecraft	Class 388 or 78
THERM or T_{H2}	2-stage thermostat Thermostat with subbase	Honeywell Honeywell	T872F1019 Q672C or D
M.D. 1, 2, and 3	Low-leakage dampers Low-voltage motors	Honeywell Honeywell	Series D640 24V M836A
ΔT (Diff. Col/Storage)	Differential controller with T_{COL} collector sensor, RB_T coldside rockbin sensor	Honeywell	R7412A1004
ΔT_{HW} (Diff. Col/H_2O)	Differential controller with T_{CHW} collector sensor for DHW and T_{H_2O} preheat tank sensor	Independent Energy	C-30 Sun Switch
T_{COL}	Remote bulb SPDT thermostat	Honeywell	T675A, 160° to 260°F Range
RB_T	Remote bulb SPDT thermostat	Dayton	Grainger 2E399
T_{CSD} or T_C	Remote bulb SPDT thermostat	Honeywell	T675A, 55° to 175°F Range
T_{H1}	Line-voltage thermostat	Dayton or Honeywell	Grainger 2E158 Grainger 2E516

TABLE 7.2, continued
AIR-HANDLING CONTROL MATERIALS

Symbol	Description	Manufacturer	Manufacturer Number
T_{HL_1}	Remote bulb SPDT thermostat	Honeywell	T675A, 160° to 260°F Range
T_{HL_2}	Remote bulb SPDT thermostat	Honeywell	T675A, 160° to 260°F Range
F_1	Collector blower	Bayley or Lau	Series BC
F_2	House blower	Bayley or Lau	Series FGP or BD
P	Heat exchanger pump	Grundfos 10gpm	UPS 20-42
$B_{1, 2}$	Buzzer	Electrical Supply	6V dc, 2 amps or less (1 amp preferred)
PS	Power source/battery backup	Ademco	#AD-1028 with maintained contact switch #2174-70

The systems shown in Figures 7.25, 7.26 and 7.27 are high voltage (115v AC), so they should be wired with a minimum of #14/2 with ground, in accordance with the National Electrical Code and local building codes. Alternate low-voltage wiring controls are shown in the field and control wiring of Figure 7.28. Both systems are connected to a line-voltage thermostat, and the auxiliary heating system has its own thermostat. The auxiliary thermostat should be set a *minimum* of 2°F below the solar thermostat. The greater the differential, the longer the time delay between the first (solar) and the second (auxiliary) stage call for heat.

The auxiliary thermostat should be set at the desired average house temperature. The solar thermostat, however, should be set just below the daytime overheating temperature. The collector should be allowed to run, collecting heat and storing it in the mass of the living space itself. Once the mass has stored as much as it can, the space will begin to overheat. The solar thermostat should be set just below this point, which can be found with experience. The higher the solar thermostat is set, the greater the differential will be between it and the auxiliary thermostat, and maximum utilization of available solar energy will be achieved.

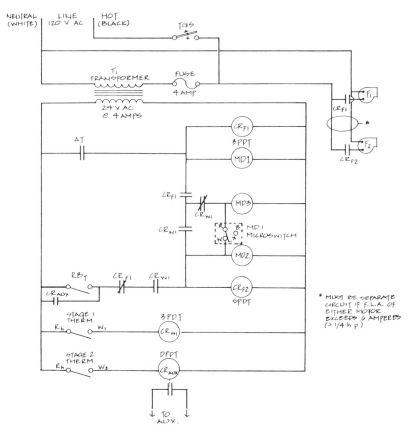

FIG. 7.9 WIRING SCHEMATIC, NEW CONSTRUCTION:
SERIES AUXILIARY WALL COLLECTOR WITH STORAGE

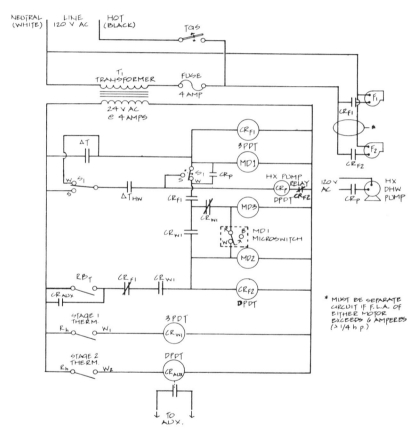

FIG. 7.10 WIRING SCHEMATIC, NEW CONSTRUCTION:
SERIES AUXILIARY WALL COLLECTOR WITH STORAGE AND DHW

MODEL-TEA
SYSTEM CONTROL WIRING

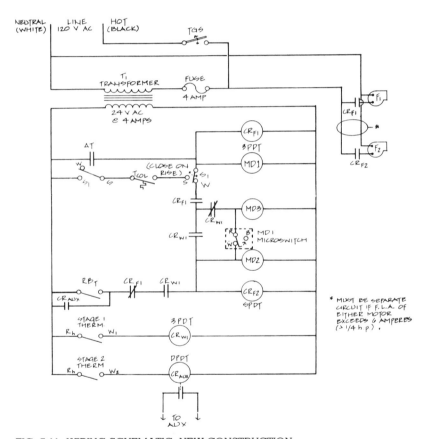

FIG. 7.11 WIRING SCHEMATIC, NEW CONSTRUCTION:
SERIES AUXILIARY ROOF COLLECTOR WITH STORAGE AND POWER VENTING

MODEL-TEA
SYSTEM CONTROL WIRING

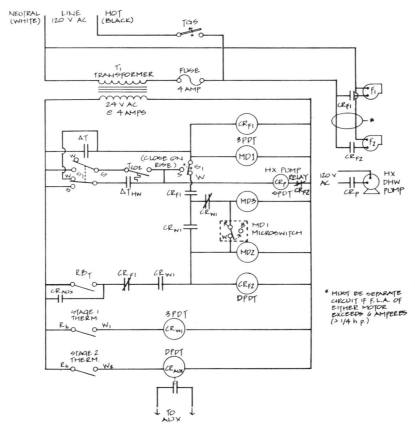

FIG. 7.12 WIRING SCHEMATIC, NEW CONSTRUCTION:
SERIES AUXILIARY ROOF COLLECTOR WITH STORAGE, DHW, AND POWER VENTING

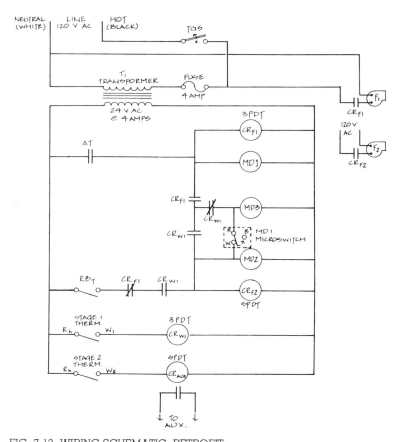

FIG. 7.13 WIRING SCHEMATIC, RETROFIT:
PARALLEL AUXILIARY WALL COLLECTOR WITH STORAGE

MODEL-TEA
SYSTEM CONTROL WIRING

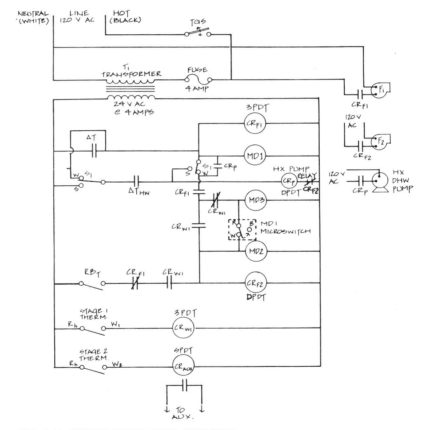

FIG. 7.14 WIRING SCHEMATIC, RETROFIT:
PARALLEL AUXILIARY WALL COLLECTOR WITH STORAGE AND DHW

MODEL-TEA
SYSTEM CONTROL WIRING

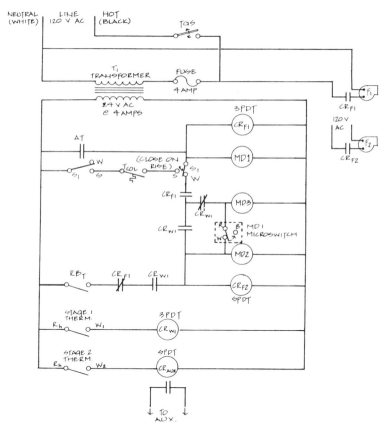

FIG. 7.15 WIRING SCHEMATIC, REFROFIT:
PARALLEL AUXILIARY ROOF COLLECTOR WITH STORAGE AND POWER VENTING

MODEL-TEA
SYSTEM CONTROL WIRING

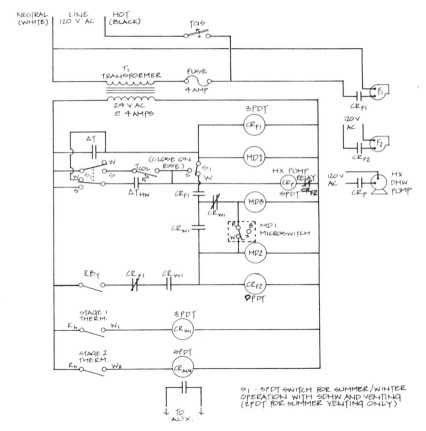

FIG. 7.16 WIRING SCHEMATIC, RETROFIT:
PARALLEL AUXILIARY ROOF COLLECTOR WITH STORAGE, DHW, AND POWER VENTING

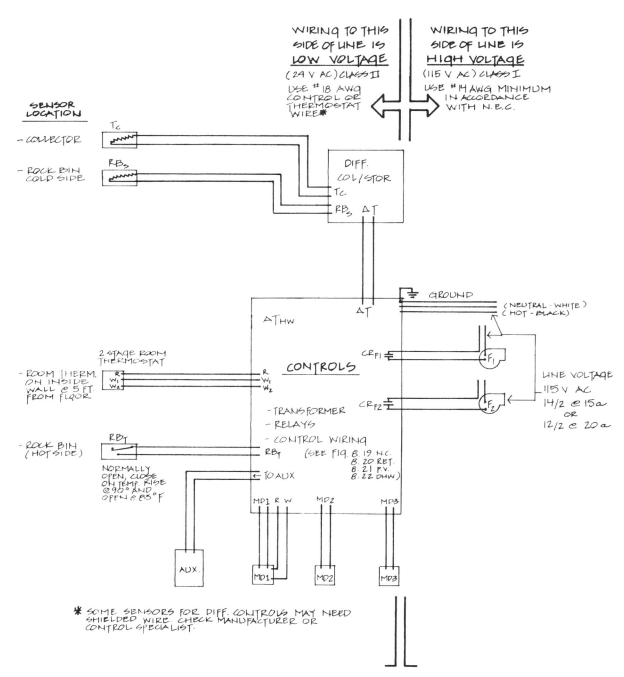

FIG. 7.17 FIELD WIRING FOR WALL COLLECTOR WITH STORAGE

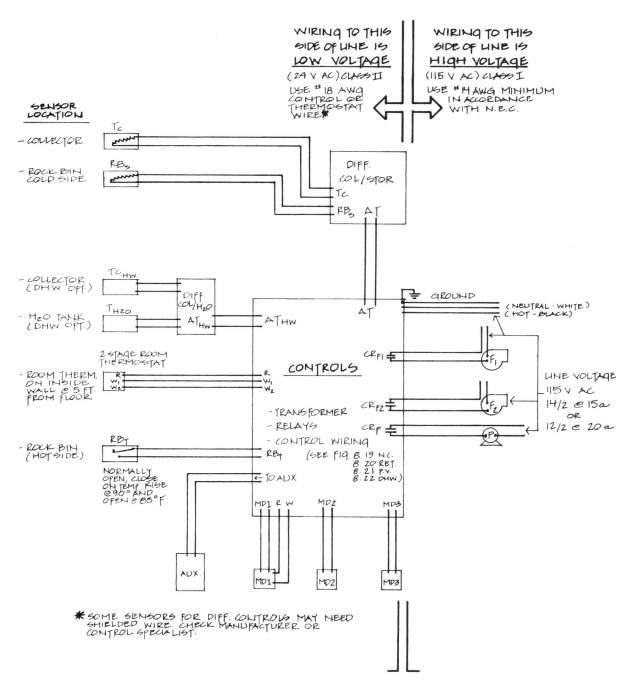

FIG. 7.18 FIELD WIRING FOR WALL COLLECTOR WITH STORAGE AND DHW

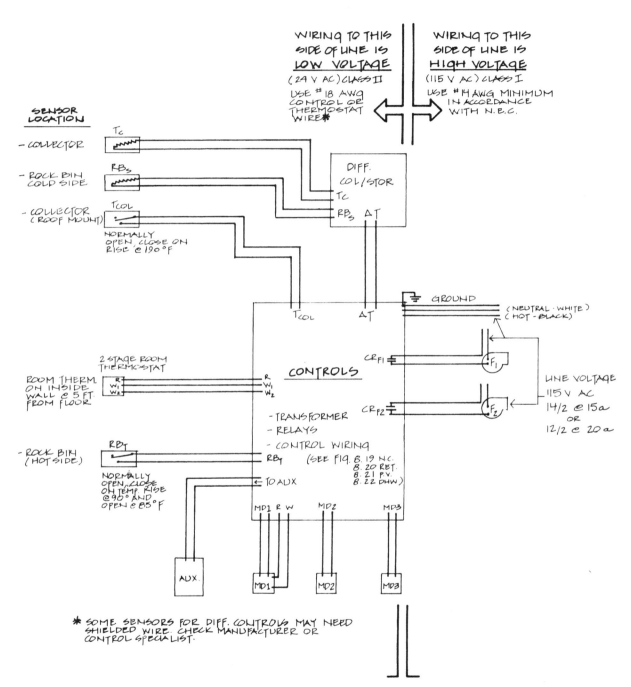

FIG. 7.19 FIELD WIRING FOR ROOF COLLECTOR
WITH STORAGE AND POWER VENTING

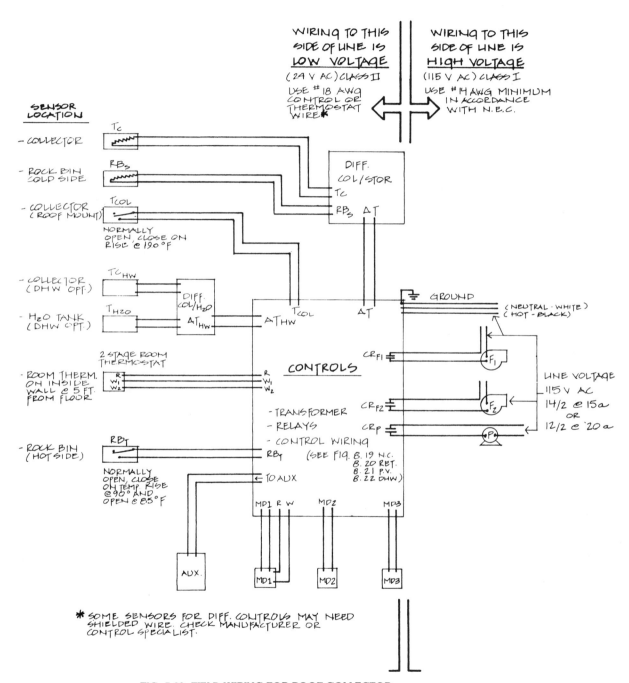

FIG. 7.20 FIELD WIRING FOR ROOF COLLECTOR
WITH STORAGE, DHW, AND POWER VENTING

MODEL-TEA
SYSTEM CONTROL WIRING

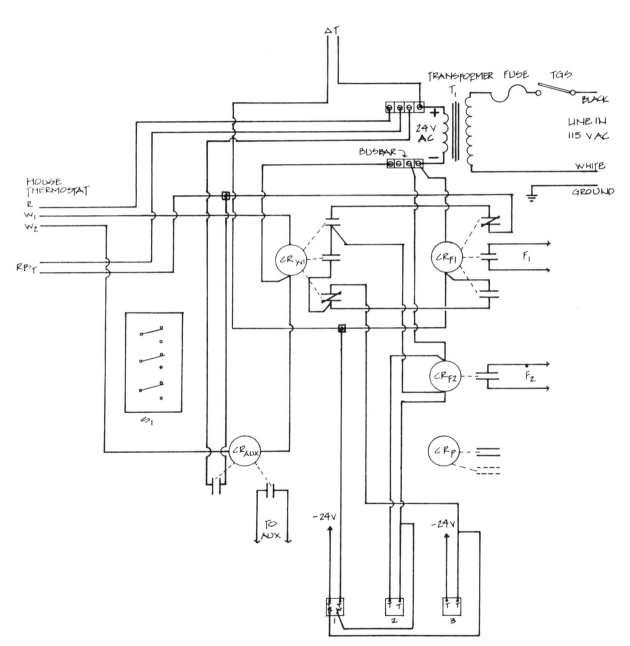

FIG. 7.21 BASIC CONTROL WIRING, NEW CONSTRUCTION:
SYSTEMS WITH STORAGE AND SERIES AUXILIARY HEATING

MODEL-TEA
SYSTEM CONTROL WIRING

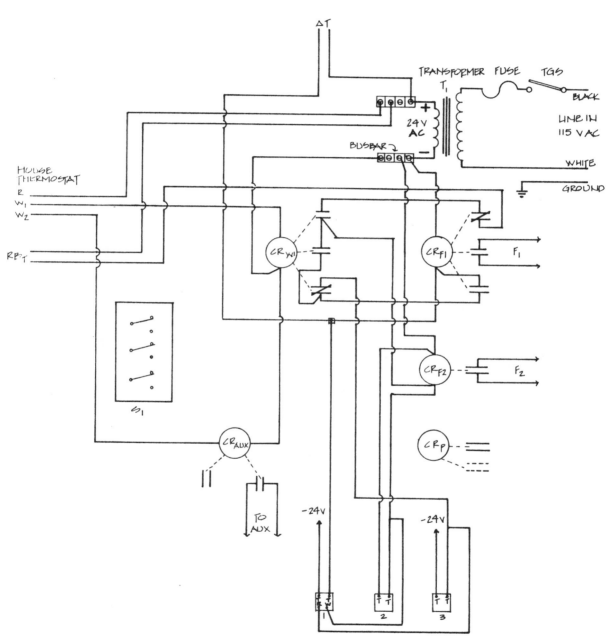

FIG. 7.22 BASIC CONTROL WIRING, RETROFIT:
SYSTEMS WITH STORAGE AND PARALLEL AUXILIARY HEATING

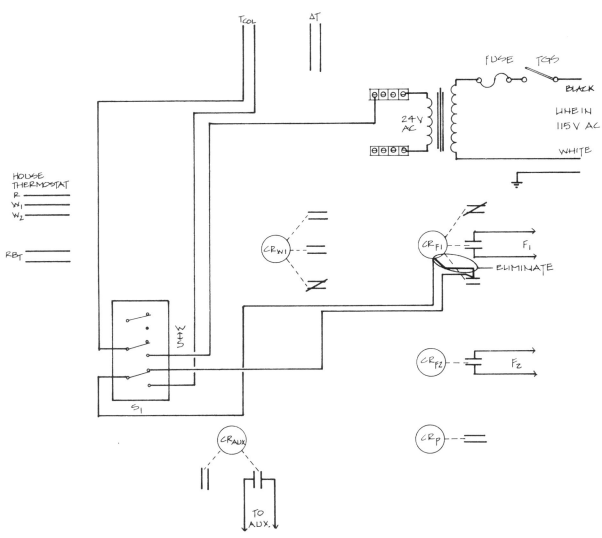

FIG. 7.23 CONTROL WIRING FOR POWER VENTING OF ROOF COLLECTORS

MODEL-TEA
SYSTEM CONTROL WIRING

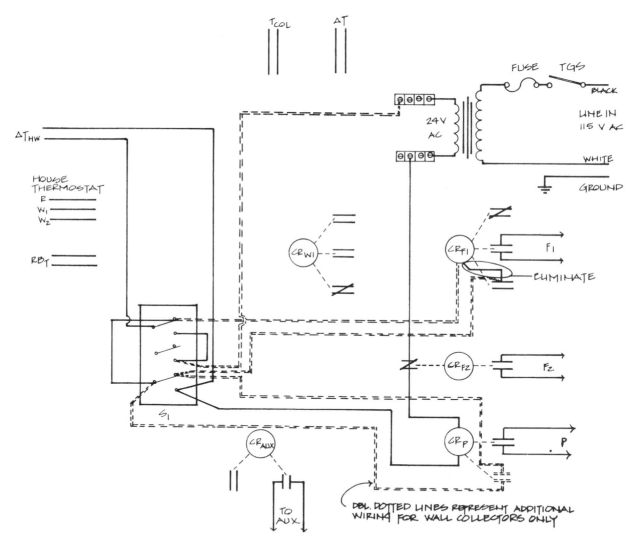

FIG. 7.24 CONTROL WIRING FOR DHW

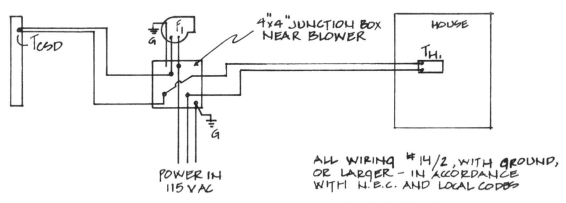

SYSTEM SCHEMATIC

WIRING SCHEMATIC

FIELD WIRING

FIG. 7.25 DAYTIME SYSTEM, WALL COLLECTOR WITHOUT STORAGE

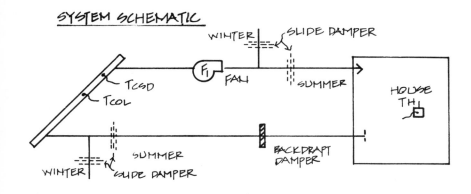

SYSTEM SCHEMATIC

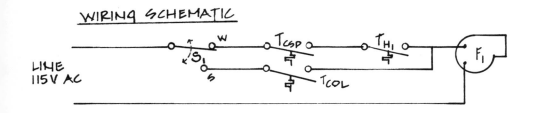

WIRING SCHEMATIC

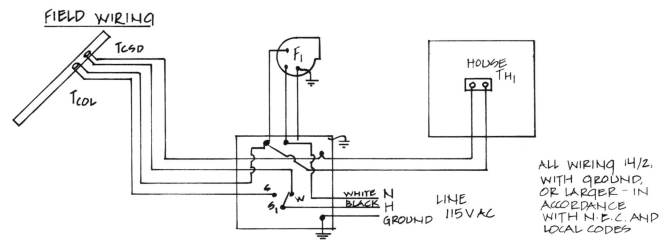

FIELD WIRING

ALL WIRING 14/2, WITH GROUND, OR LARGER - IN ACCORDANCE WITH N.E.C. AND LOCAL CODES

FIG. 7.26 DAYTIME SYSTEM, ROOF COLLECTOR WITHOUT STORAGE, BUT WITH POWER VENTING

SYSTEM SCHEMATIC

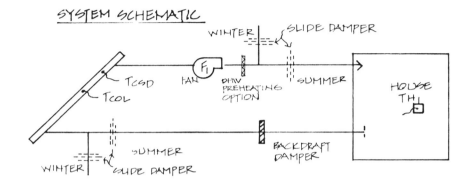

WIRING SCHEMATIC

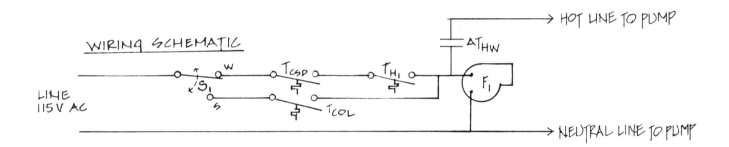

FIELD WIRING

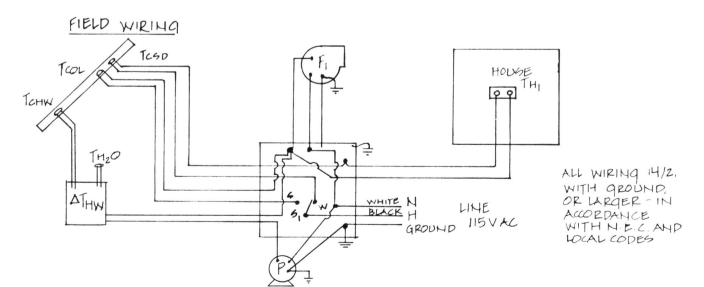

ALL WIRING 14/2, WITH GROUND, OR LARGER - IN ACCORDANCE WITH N.E.C. AND LOCAL CODES

FIG. 7.27 DAYTIME SYSTEM, ROOF COLLECTOR WITHOUT STORAGE, BUT WITH POWER VENTING AND DHW

MODEL-TEA
SYSTEM CONTROL WIRING

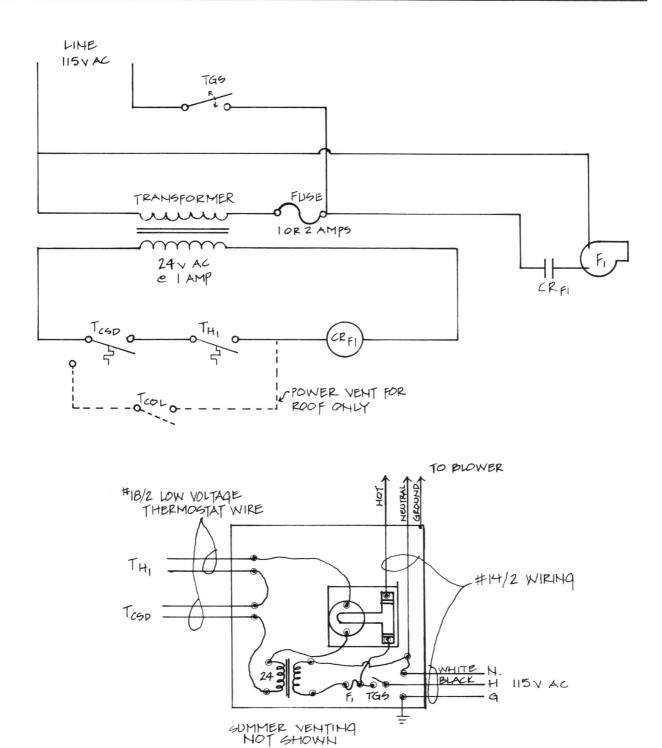

FIG. 7.28 DAYTIME SYSTEM, LOW-VOLTAGE CONTROL ALTERNATIVE

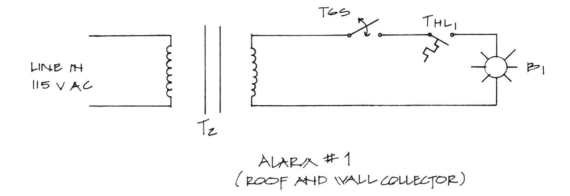

ALARM #1
(ROOF AND WALL COLLECTOR)

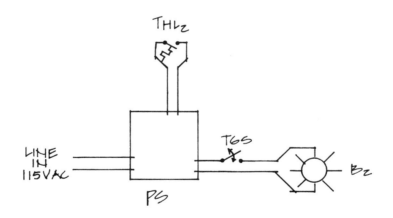

ALARM #2
(ROOF COLLECTOR ONLY)

FIG. 7.29 WIRING FOR TWO-STAGE OVERHEATING ALARMS (PS: POWER SOURCE/
CHARGING CIRCUIT FOR OPERATION DURING POWER FAILURE)

CHAPTER 8

DESIGN
OPTIONS

8.1 COMMERCIAL AIR HANDLERS

T.E.A. studied commercially available air handlers, and decided instead to feature a site-assembled air handler in its system. The design for the MODEL-TEA conventional air-handling system is less expensive, more flexible, and has a more effective control strategy than most commercial air handlers. (A list of available air handlers is included in Appendix A.2.)

However, two commercial air handlers are available for approximately $1300, and thus are potentially attractive alternatives to a site-built air-handling system. The Delta-H Air-Handler uses a standard blower but an innovative damper design. It provides standard three-mode operation and comes with a complete control system and a DHW coil. The other product, the CSI "No Frills," uses conventional dampers, but a propeller fan rather than a blower. It also provides the standard three-mode operation and comes with a complete control package, but the $1300 price does not include the DHW option. CSI sells a separate complete DHW package, including the coil, and control board with differential and pump, for roughly $1000.

T.E.A. has no direct field experience with either product. If they are successful, they offer the major benefits of vastly simplifying system installation and reducing costs. Whereas the MODEL-TEA site-assembled system requires a knowledgeable professional to install the control system, these two air handlers have the controls already connected. The consumer must weigh low cost and ease of installation on one hand, against the low risk of standard components and a conventional design on the other.

8.2 MODEL-TEA INNOVATIVE SYSTEM

The system illustrated in Figure 8.1 utilizes a one-way rock bed. This system can be built at a potentially lower cost, but it is more critically dependent upon precise sizing and engineering, and requires extensive integration with the building design. For these reasons, this system should not be used unless the services of an experienced solar designer are available.

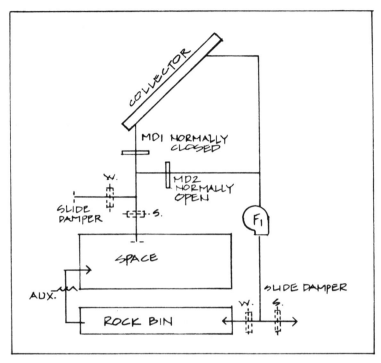

FIG. 8.1 SCHEMATIC FOR MODEL-TEA INNOVATIVE SYSTEM

The one-way rock bed allows a much simpler air-handling system, and thorough building integration permits major savings in ductwork. The system has two modes. In the first mode, *collection*, air is drawn from the house to the collector, heated, blown through the rock bed and returned to the house. In the second mode, *storage to house*, air is drawn from the house to the rock bed, heated, and delivered back to the house. Air flow through the rock bed is in the same direction in both modes. The auxiliary heater is located in series between the rock bed and the living space, and whenever the solar-heated air cannot meet the house heating demand, the auxiliary boosts the air temperature.

The basic concept of this system is that the one-way rock bed provides a time delay: the collector primarily heats the rock bed during the day, by the end of the day the rock bed is saturated, and during the night the bed heats the house. The sizing of the

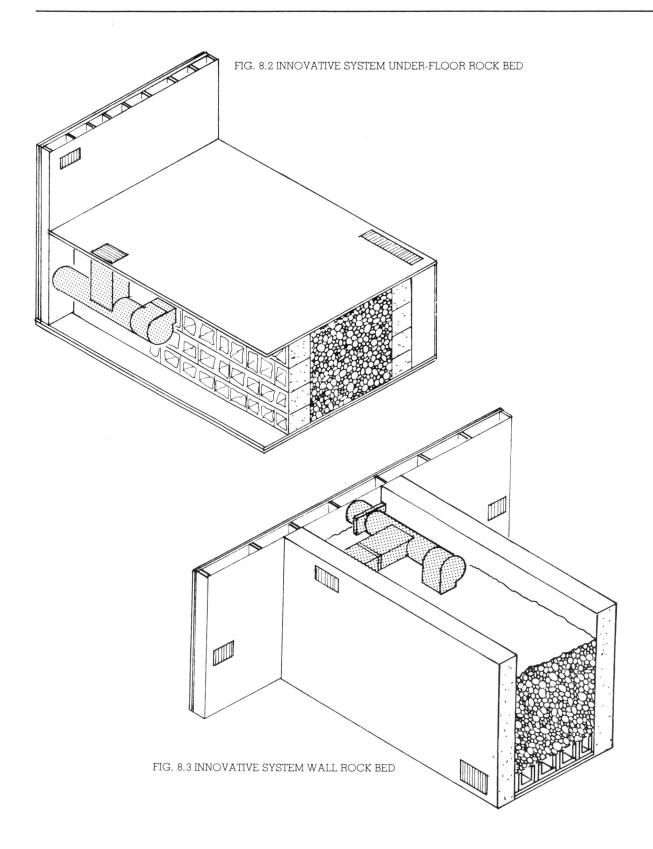

FIG. 8.2 INNOVATIVE SYSTEM UNDER-FLOOR ROCK BED

FIG. 8.3 INNOVATIVE SYSTEM WALL ROCK BED

TABLE 8.1
MODE SCHEDULE FOR INNOVATIVE SYSTEM

Mode	Fan	MD1	MD2	Aux.	Signals
Space/coll/rock bin/space	On	O	C	Off	Δt
Space/rock bin/space	On	C	O	Off	W_1
Auxiliary stage 1	On	O	C	On	W_2, ΔT
Auxiliary stage 2	On	C	O	On	W_2
Standby	Off	C	O	Off	—

rock bed is very critical. Too small a bed would cause early saturation and possible overheating of the living space in the afternoon. Too large a bed would result in low-temperature air being delivered to the house in the evening. T.E.A. conducted computer simulations of year-long one-way rock bed performance to determine optimum numbers for air flow rate and rock bed size. The best combination is approximately an air flow rate of 3 CFM per ft² of collector and a rock bed size of 2 ft³ per ft² of

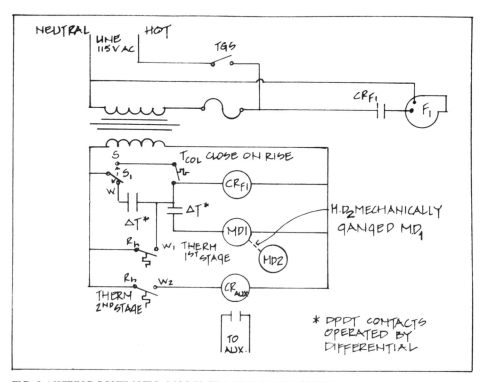

FIG. 8.4 WIRING SCHEMATIC, MODEL-TEA INNOVATIVE SYSTEM

collector. These numbers represent compromises between conflicting goals. For example, lowering the air flow rate results in higher collector outlet temperatures, reducing collector efficiency, but producing more useful heating temperatures. Because of the critical engineering required, and the variety of ways this system can be integrated into a new design, any installation will benefit from the services of an experienced solar consultant.

8.3 HIGH-TEMPERATURE RIGID INSULATION

In the development of the collector design, T.E.A. was very concerned with potential problems caused by exposing wood to moderately high temperatures for long periods of time. The project staff consulted with both the American Plywood Association and the U.S. Department of Agriculture, Forest Products Laboratory, in order to become better acquainted with the current understanding of the relevant wood properties. Wood can endure very long exposure to temperatures as high as 200°F without significant degradation. But wood exposed continuously to 300°F for one year will undergo major weight loss and probably begin to char; when the wood has charred the probability of spontaneous combustion increases significantly.

The MODEL-TEA collector will normally operate below 200°F, but if it were allowed to stagnate, the roof collector could reach temperatures of 300°F or higher for short periods of time (a few hours per day). At night the collector temperature would always be down to ambient temperature. If the roof collector were allowed to stagnate throughout the summer, it could spend a total of between 500 and 1000 hours (depending upon climate) above 250°F. For this reason, the roof collector is always power vented. Vertical wall collectors are not subject to many hours at high stagnation temperatures and therefore do not require power venting.

If the power venting system fails, the collector will reach high summer stagnation temperatures, roughly 300°F, but short exposures to these temperatures will not have deleterious effects. Since Thermo-ply is the only material between the absorber and the wood rafters, the wood will reach a temperature very close to that of the absorber. T.E.A. does not believe this to be a problem, so long as proper power venting is employed. In some areas, however, codes may require more insulation between any wood structure and the collector. If insulation is required, it must be chosen carefully.

There are a number of rigid insulation materials available, but most cannot be used in the MODEL-TEA collector. Polyurethane, polystyrene, and isocyanurate insulations are not acceptable, since they are quite flammable and release fumes and toxic gases. Use of one of these materials under the MODEL-TEA absorber would be particularly dangerous due to proximity to the air stream through the collector. Foamglass is not flammable and could be used under the Thermo-ply; however, it is extremely abrasive, making it very unpleasant to work with.

Another available material is Isophenol, a rigid phenolic foam. It has much better flame resistance than polystyrene or polyurethane, and a very low emission of smoke or noxious fumes in case of a fire. Since Isophenol is available with a foil facing, its use eliminates the need for the Thermo-ply. In addition, Isophenol is relatively inexpensive—$0.28/bf plus an extra $0.15/ft² for the foil face. The material is fairly fragile, as is foamglass, and requires careful handling. Even though the foil-faced material is used, the insulation is exposed to the air stream at the manifold cutouts. Since the material easily flakes and crumbles, these exposed areas should be covered with special high-temperature tape which can endure stagnation temperatures.

Perhaps the material most commonly used for collector installations is rigid fiberglass industrial insulation. A typical example is the Owens-Corning 700 series, which has a maximum operating temperature of 450°F. All the major manufacturers of fiberglass insulation have similiar industrial board products. The builder should note that the introduction of any rigid insulation to the area under the absorber will change some of the dimensions given in the construction drawings, and the builder will have to determine the appropriate new dimensions.

8.4 ALUMINUM BATTENS

T.E.A. believes that the use of wood for inner collector battens presents no significant problem. For the reasons discussed in the previous section, the wooden battens should not suffer any serious long-term degradation due to collector temperatures. However, if desired, these battens can be replaced with metal, thereby eliminating all wood from the collector. Aluminum must be used, not steel, since galvanic corrosion could exist between the aluminum absorber and steel battens. The substitution of aluminum battens for wood will raise the materials cost of the collector approximately $0.76/ft^2.

In the standard MODEL-TEA collector, the wooden battens are fastened to the absorber ribs, not the valleys. This is done because the compressible wood can make an airtight seal over the absorber rib. If, instead, the batten screws were fastened to the valleys, the Thermo-ply would be perforated and there is a possibility of the aluminum absorber and the Thermo-ply becoming slightly separated by the screw. While there normally would not be any air flow in the valley, there would be some possibility of leakage. Thus, T.E.A. decided it would be more prudent to fasten the wooden battens to the ribs. But aluminum battens do not seal as well to the ribs and, since most of the air flow is under the ribs, it is probably safer to fasten these battens to the valleys. (Sources for aluminum battens are listed in Appendix A.2.)

APPENDIX A

MATERIALS
AND SUPPLIES

A.1 MATERIALS

The MODEL-TEA collector is constructed from standard materials, including caulks, paints, sheathings, fasteners, insulations, industrial sidings, sheet metal, and glazings. Most of these materials are available in a variety of formulations and grades from numerous manufacturers. However, all are *not* suitable for use in a solar collector, which is subjected to UV radiation, high temperatures, and large temperature fluctuations. Many materials which perform well in ordinary building construction will fail in solar collector applications.

This section presents a brief discussion of each class of material, followed by a list of materials that, based on manufacturers' data, and in some cases limited testing, should provide adequate service in the intended applications.

The materials for the rock bin are standard construction materials which should be available from local suppliers. On the other hand, the materials for the air-handling and control systems are very specific, and should be ordered only after you read Appendix A.2.

This list is not all-inclusive. New materials are constantly being developed and introduced. However, before substituting, the user should consult knowledgeable sources to ensure that the new materials will perform satisfactorily.

Sheathing/Absorber Back

On the MODEL-TEA collector, the sheathing serves as the absorber backplate. Thermo-ply, a pressure-laminated, foil-faced, structural sheathing, is recommended. Thermo-ply, unlike plywood, does not outgas and is not as easily degraded by long-term exposure to high temperatures. In addition, the low weight and foil face reduce the capacitance effects in the collector. A collector with a low thermal capacitance is desirable, since most of the heat stored in the collector is lost when the collector shuts off at night or during cloudy periods.

Thermo-ply is available in several grades. The Super Strength grade (Blue) can be used without corner bracing on 24 in. o.c. framing. It is strongly recommended over Structural

Grade (Red). It may, however, be difficult to obtain in some areas of the country.

Thermo-ply can be installed without painting the foil face. Although painting the Thermo-ply would increase efficiency by 3 to 4%, it would also increase the capacitance of the collector, resulting in little net increase in performance. It should also be noted that Thermo-ply is easier to handle and significantly less expensive than plywood. Experience at T.E.A. indicates that the use of CDX plywood will result in significant leakage from the collector.

Caulk

Caulking should make an airtight and vaporproof seal between two materials, adhere to a moving joint, and withstand weathering, ultra-violet degradation, and extreme temperature variation. Caulks should be able to tolerate continuous temperatures of 140°F, and intermittent temperatures of 200–300°F. In the construction of the MODEL-TEA collector, caulks must remain relatively fluid and tack-free for at least a half hour to allow proper positioning and fastening of materials.

All caulks should be applied to clean, dry surfaces. The aluminum absorber plate and the Thermo-ply should be cleaned with a solvent to remove oils and greases. Wood should be clean and dry. Some caulk manufacturers recommend the use of primers, but primers are probably not essential for the type of bonds used in the MODEL-TEA collector.

One-part urethane (polyurethane) caulks appear to be the best all-around caulks for use in the MODEL-TEA collector. They can tolerate continuous temperatures of over 275°F, and satisfy all the other criteria. Urethanes can be applied without priming on all surfaces, and they remain tack-free sufficiently long to allow proper positioning of materials.

Standard silicone construction adhesives (such as GE 1200, Dow Corning Silicone Rubber Sealant and Dow Corning 790) are unsatisfactory for use in the layered joints of the MODEL-TEA collector. These caulks skin over in approximately 10 minutes or less and prevent satisfactory "sandwich" type joints such as the seal between the Thermo-ply and the manifold pans.

(These silicone caulks are suitable for use in the glazing details. However, if they are ordered for this application, care must be taken to ensure that they are not inadvertently used in other construction steps.)

Polysulfide caulks may also be used in the MODEL-TEA collector. They satisfy all criteria, and can tolerate a continuous temperature of approximately 250°F. However, primers may be necessary; manufacturers' directions should be followed. Butyl rubber caulks are satisfactory in most respects. However, their life is estimated at only 7 to 10 years in normal applications, and might be less in solar collector applications. Consequently, they are not recommended for use in the MODEL-TEA collector. Acrylic terpolymer caulks, such as Tremco MONO, are unsatisfactory due to excessive degradation at normal collector operating temperatures. Low-performance caulks such as oil base, acrylic latex, and other inexpensive formulations do not satisfy the criteria and are unsatisfactory.

Aluminum Siding Absorber

Aluminum siding is available from several manufacturers in 4-in. rib and 8-in. rib. The choice of rib type depends on the length of the absorber plate (the distance between manifolds). If this distance is greater than 16 feet, 8-in. rib should be used to avoid excessive pressure drops. This will be the case for most roof installations. If the distance is less than 12 feet, 4-in. rib should be used. This will be the case for most wall installations. For absorbers between 12 and 16 feet, either rib design may be used.

Absorber sections should be ordered in lengths sufficient to cover the collector from manifold to manifold; whether from end manifold to end manifold, or from end manifold to center manifold.

Aluminum siding is available with two finishes: mill-finish aluminum and factory painted. The mill-finish aluminum has an oil residue on its surface and must be degreased prior to painting. It must be primed and painted with an appropriate black paint.

The factory painted panels are not available with a black finish and must be repainted. There are conflicting opinions from manufacturers regarding the procedure. T.E.A. applied Nextel epoxy directly to the factory painted absorber without primer. There was no evidence of problems following a 30-day stagnation test, but long-term durability is unknown.

Galvanized steel siding can be substituted for aluminum siding as long as the rib width and dimensions are the same. It is difficult to find and is heavier than aluminum. However, less energy is consumed in the manufacture of galvanized steel than aluminum.

Rubber Closure Strips

EPDM rubber end closure strips are available from the supplier of the ribbed siding. "Inside" closures, which fit *under* the absorber, must be specified. ("Outside" closures are available, but will not fit.) Only 100% EPDM closures should be used. Closures which are blends of EPDM and other materials (neoprene and SBR) are not acceptable, since they degrade at lower temperatures.

Smoke Bombs

It is very important to do a smoke test before glazing the collector. Improper installation of the end closures or inadvertent omission of caulk can result in significant leaks which can easily go unnoticed unless a smoke test is performed. Leaks reduce collector efficiency and must be eliminated.

Although smoke can be produced by burning burlap or using toxic rodent smoke bombs, it is best to purchase smoke bombs specially developed for detecting leaks. Superior Signal Company, Inc., makes a suitable smoke bomb for this purpose.

Absorber Surface Preparation

It is very important to clean the absorber surface thoroughly to insure good adhesion of the paint. Machining oils must be removed from the surface of mill-finish aluminum, using a degreaser. Trisodium-phosphate (TSP) is a good degreaser, available at many hardware stores. Precautions should be taken to protect the eyes and skin when using degreasers.

Just prior to painting the absorber, it should be wiped with the paint solvent in order to remove residues from the degreaser or from handling the absorber. The absorber can be painted either before or after installation. A surface painted before installation is likely to be scratched and smeared with caulk and will usually require considerable touchup. Therefore, painting after installation is recommended.

Paint

Paints used in solar collector applications should be highly absorptive to solar radiation and are usually flat-black. Paints must be able to tolerate UV radiation, continuous temperatures of 140°F, intermittent temperatures of from 200–300°F, and diurnal expansion and contraction.

They must have good adherence to the absorber surface. Manufacturers' recommendations for surface preparation, priming, and applications of the paint should be carefully followed. Evaporation of the solvent during drying of paints (outgassing) causes a film to be deposited on the glazing, decreasing transmittance and collector efficiency. For this reason, it is essential that the paint be fully dry *before* the collector glazing is added.

Acrylic enamels and oil-base paints are widely available, easy to apply, and durable. However, solvent evaporates during drying and at least two full days should be allowed for drying before the glazing assembly is installed. Epoxy paints consist of two components which must be mixed prior to application. The paint cures by chemical reaction, and outgassing is minimized. Epoxy paints should be used if the construction schedule does not allow several days for drying.

Paints identified as "selective" have recently been introduced. In fact, they are only partially selective. For example, Sun-In has an emissivity of 0.68, compared to an emissivity of 0.10 for an electrochemically deposited selective surface such as "black chrome."

Wood

Good, straight, dry wood should be used for interior battens; spruce or fir is recommended. Pine should *not* be used, due to the resin which may be given off in outgassing. Redwood is also *not* recommended, since redwood forests are being decimated by overproduction.

The outer battens on the wall collector can be constructed from wood or aluminum. Wood is less expensive but requires more maintenance and has been observed to warp and crack. Wood is recommended only if dictated by aesthetic requirements.

Glazing

The most important properties sought in a glazing system are: (1) resistance to degradation from heat, light and weather; (2) high transmittance to solar radiation and low transmittance to infrared; (3) attractive appearance; (4) ease of handling and fabrication; and (5) low cost.

Glass is clearly the best material for glazing a solar collector. It is unaffected by heat, ultraviolet radiation, and weather; properly installed, it should last indefinitely. Glass is optically flat, and is generally regarded as the most attractive glazing.

Since collectors may be subjected to severe thermal stresses, wind and snow loads, and impact from hail and other missiles, only fully tempered glass is acceptable. The use of double-glazed insulating glass units simplifies the installation of two-layer glazing systems. Insulating glass units, 46 x 96 in., constructed with two panes of $3/16$-in. glass and a ½ in. air space, are specified in the construction drawings for the wall collector. AFG Industries, Inc., markets insulating glass units available wth three types of low-iron glass: Solatex, Sunadex, and Clearlite. The best choice appears to be Solatex. Its transmittance (0.90) is slightly less than that of Sunadex (0.915), but its cost is at least 20% less. Both materials have a textured surface which diffuses reflected light, eliminating glare and mirrorlike reflections. The elimination of these reflections is an important aesthetic factor for solar collectors; it makes the collectors less noticeable and avoids troubling neighbors with the glare. The overall effect of textured glass with a black absorber underneath, is a smooth, dull, near-black surface. A third glass, AFG Clearlite, has a normal flat surface, resulting in both glare and perfect reflections for situations where that is desired. This material has a transmittance of only 0.82.

The cost of AFG insulating glass units is dependent on the quantity purchased. The purchase of less than one standard case of 25 double-glazed 34 x 96 in. Solatex units will cost $4.90/ft²; purchase of a standard case costs only $4.56/ft². Since it is unlikely that 25 units could be used on a single building, it will be necessary to purchase glass for two or three buildings to achieve the substantial discount.

An alternative is to purchase standard insulating glass units from local suppliers. Only insulating glass panels with an edge detail that allows the inner pane to expand relative to the outer panes is acceptable. Insulating glass with metal or glass edges has a tendency to crack in solar applications and must not be used. It is advisable to consult with the manufacturer regarding the maximum temperature to which the unit can safely be subjected (it should be at least 300°F). The price of these units range from $2.75 to $5.00/ft², depending on the supplier. However, they are not low-iron glass, and they will reduce collector efficiency by about 6%. This is worth about $1.25/ft² in fuel over a 20-year period. It should also be noted that most standard units are only available in 34 x 76 in. units. Their use will require a modification in the construction plans and result in a smaller collector area per length of wall.

Another alternative is to purchase and install two individual panes of glass. However, this approach is more difficult and unless properly installed, is unlikely to result in as durable and as attractive a system.

Several manufacturers have developed fiberglass-reinforced polyester (FRP) glazing materials for use on solar collectors. The materials are formulated to provide resistance to ultraviolet and thermal degradation. Although FRP glazings appear cloudy, their solar transmittance (0.84–0.90) is only slightly less than low-iron glass. Kalwall's Sun-lite and Vistron's "Filon" are two commercially available fiberglass-reinforced polyester glazings.

Sun-lite is available in 4 and 5-foot-wide rolls in thicknesses of 0.025, 0.040 and 0.060 inches. It is a popular material for site-built collectors since it is easy to cut, drill, and install. There are, however two problems inherent with Sun-lite. The most noticeable is one of appearance: when applied from rolls, it does not lie flat, resulting in a wavy appearance. This is aggravated as the collector heats up, due to Sun-lite's relatively large coefficient of thermal expansion. T.E.A. is concerned that the appearance will get progressively worse as the material continues to undergo thermal cycling. In order to minimize this problem, Kalwall has developed double-glazed panels where the Sun-lite is "stretched" onto an aluminum frame. The theory is that since aluminum and Sun-lite have nearly the same coefficient of thermal expansion, the glazing will be tight regardless of the temperature. T.E.A. has used the panels and finds that the wavy effect is reduced, but not eliminated.

The second problem relates to thermal degradation at high temperatures. Kalwall notes that Sun-lite experiences losses in transmission of 1%, 3% and 11%, when exposed to temperatures of 150°F, 200°F, and 300°F respectively for 300 hours. Since summer stagnation temperatures are between 200 and 300°F, some method of ventilating excess heat is required to protect Sun-lite.

Filon is an acrylic-fortified polyester reinforced with fiberglass. The panels are clad with a layer of Tedlar polyvinyl-fluoride to provide protection from ultraviolet reduction and weathering. Filon is available in flat or corrugated sheets, 4 ft wide and up to 16 ft long, in various thicknesses. Use of the corrugated materials may minimize the wavy appearance problem; however, T.E.A. has had no experience with this material. Filon, like Sun-lite, must be vented to protect it from thermal degradation under stagnation conditions. Sun-lite and Filon sheet are not recommended for glazing either the wall or roof version of the MODEL-TEA collector due to their wavy appearance and concerns about the long-term effects of thermal cycling.

Rigid plastic glazings have high resistance to impact and fracture, good ease of handling and fabrication, and attractive appearance. Most of the products can be categorized as either acrylics of polycarbonates.

Acrylics have a slightly higher transmittance than tempered

water-white glass, and exhibit good resistance to ultra-violet light and weathering. They are usually clear and are as attractive as glass if they are not scratched.

There are several major disadvantages of acrylics in solar applications. Acrylics begin to soften at 180°F and melt at 250°F; they must not be used without fail-safe stagnation protection. Further, they have a very large coefficient of expansion and tend to "bow-in" on the hot side. T.E.A. tested Acrylite SDP, a double-wall acrylic glazing, on a collector module. Supported on 4-ft centers using the manufacturer's glazing system, the material bowed in ¾ in., touching the absorber plate and exerting considerable stresses on the glazing supports at normal collector operation temperatures.

Polycarbonates are stronger than acrylics and have a somewhat higher melting point. However, they have lower transmittance and suffer from ultraviolet degradation. Polycarbonates also have a high coefficient of thermal expansion and bow inward toward the absorber plate.

Acrylics and polycarbonates are not recommended for site-fabricated collector applications because of their low melting points and their high thermal expansion at collector operating temperatures.

Plastic films offer high transmittance and are relatively inexpensive. Two common materials are Dupont's Teflon and Tedlar. Teflon has excellent resistance to temperature. However, it has a high coefficient of expansion and tends to sag when installed as an inner glazing. It is also difficult to handle, bowing between supports and sticking to surfaces due to its tendency to acquire a static charge. In addition, it is relatively transparent to infrared radiation from the absorber plate, which reduces its effectiveness. There are similar problems with Tedlar; in addition, Tedlar becomes brittle with thermally accelerated ultraviolet degradation. Plastic films are not recommended for glazing the MODEL-TEA collector.

Glazing System

The glazing system chosen to fasten glass to the MODEL-TEA collector consists of two layers of EPDM strips and an aluminum bar cap. Such a system is sold by CY/RO Industries as their Universal Glazing System (U.G.S.). This can be purchased directly from CY/RO.

It may also be possible to site-build a similar glazing system by purchasing flat EPDM strips from a manufacturer (such as Tremco), and buying aluminum bar stock separately. For a vertical wall collector, wood could be used for this outer batten, instead of aluminum. The wood will not be as durable, but it may be more aesthetically pleasing.

A.2 MANUFACTURERS AND DISTRIBUTORS

COLLECTORS

Thermo-ply

Simplex Products Group, 3000 W. Beecher Road, P.O. Box 10, Adrian, MI 49221.

DISTRIBUTORS

Local building-supply companies

Aluminum Industrial Siding

Alcoa, 1501 Alcoa Building, Pittsburgh, PA 15219.

DISTRIBUTORS

Long Island Tinsmith, 111 & Jamaica Streets, Richmond Hill, NY 11418.
H.S. Westcover, 5746 Scenic View Drive, Bethel, PA 15102 and 3642 Daisy Court, Brunswick, OH 44212.

Wisconsin Bridge and Iron, 5023 N. 35th Street, Milwaukee, WI
53209.
Yancy & Jamieson, Inc., 4725 Bakers Ferry Road, Atlanta, GA
30336.

Reynolds Metals Company, 10 Presidential Boulevard, Bala
Cynwyd, PA 19004.

DISTRIBUTORS

Contact manufacturer

EPDM Rubber Closure Strips

Use only 100% EPDM; normally available from distributor of
aluminum siding, but can contact manufacturer:
American National Rubber, Huntington, WV

Aluminum or Stainless Steel Fasteners

Albany Products Company, 145 Woodward Avenue, South
Norwalk, CT 06852.
Idea Development, Inc., P.O. Box 44, Antrim, NH 03440.

Sensors

See Air-Handling for:
1. ΔT collector/storage; Honeywell sensor
2. Remote bulb SPDT; Dayton thermostat
3. Remote bulb, Honeywell sensors
See DHW preheat for: ΔT collector/DHW preheat tank Honeywell
sensor

Caulking

URETHANE

Sears Best Caulk, Catalog #30G38211, available from Sears
stores.

PR365, Products Research & Chemical Corporation, Chemical Products Division, 410-416 Jersey Avenue, Gloucester City, NJ 08030.

SILICONE

Silglaze, Silicone Products Department, General Electric Company, Waterford, NY 12188.

POLYSULFIDE

One-part, Type One (non-sag), Thiokol Corporation, P.O. Box 8296, 930 Lower Ferry Road, Trenton, NJ 08650.

Paint

EPOXY

Nextel Black 101-C10 and 110-C10, 3M Company, Decorative Products Division, 3M Center, St. Paul, MN 55101.

OTHER

Rust-Oleum 412, Rust-Oleum Corporation, 2301 Oakton Street, Evanston, IL 60204.
Sun-In, Solar Usage Now, Inc., 350 E. Tiffin Street, Bascom, OH 44809.
Pyromark 800, Tempil Division, Big Three Industries, Inc., 2901 Hamilton Boulevard, South Plainfield, NJ 07080.

SELECTIVE

Sun-In #7858 (graphite base), Solar Usage Now, Inc., P.O. Box 306, Bascom, OH 44809.

Smoke Bomb

Superior Signal Company, Inc., W. Greystone Road, Spots-
wood, NJ 08884.

Glazing

SINGLE-PANE SOLAR GLASS

Marketing Manager, Solar Energy Products Department, AFG
Industries, Inc., P.O. Box 929, Kingsport, TN 37662.
C-E Glass, Combustion Engineering, Inc., 825 Hylton Road,
Pennsauken, NJ 08110.
Solakleer, General Glass, 270 North Avenue, New Rochelle, NY
10801.

INSULATED SOLAR GLASS

Gayle Herwig or Eric Rapp, Cardinal Insulating Glass Co., 7115
W. Lake Street, Minneapolis, MN 55426.
C-E Glass, Combustion Engineering, Inc., 825 Hylton Road,
Pennsauken, NJ 08110.

PRE-SHIMMED GLAZING TAPE

Tremco 440, Tremco, 10701 Shaker Boulevard, Cleveland, OH
44104.

NEOPRENE GLAZING GASKETS

Tremco, 10701 Shaker Boulevard, Cleveland, OH 44104.

CY/RO UNIVERSAL GLAZING SYSTEM

CY/RO Industries, 697 Route 46, Clifton, NJ 07015.

EXTRUDED ALUMINUM BATTEN WITH EPDM INSERTS

Idea Development, Inc., P.O. Box 44, Antrim, NH 03440.

ANODIZING

H. A. Leed, 75 Leeder Hill Drive, Hamden, CT 06514.

ENAMELING

Porce-Len, Inc., P.O. Box 4328, Hamden, CT 06514.

ALUMINUM BATTENS AND CHANNELS

N. J. Aluminum Plant, 1007 Jersey Avenue, P.O. Box 73, North
Brunswick, NJ 08902.

ROCK BIN

Metal Lath

Milcor ¾ in. STAY-RIB (self-furring metal lath), Milcor Division,
Inryco Inc., 4101 W. Burnham Street, P.O. Box 393,
Milwaukee, WI 53201.

Insulation

Styrofoam TG (extruded polystyrene)[1], Dow Chemical U.S.A.,
Styrofoam Brand Products, 2020 Dow Center, Midland, MI
48640.
Foamglas (cellular glass), Pittsburgh Corning Corp., 800
Presque Isle Dr., Pittsburgh, PA 15239.
Foamular (extruded polystyrene)[1], United States Gypsum Co.,
101 South Wacker Drive, Chicago, IL 60606.
Industrial Insulation 700 Series, Owens/Corning Fiberglas
Corp., Mechanical Products Division, Fiberglas Tower,
Toledo, OH 43659.
Isophenol (phenolic resin), Lisi America Inc., 600 Prospect
Avenue, Piscataway, NJ 08854.

[1] To be used on cover of *rock bin* only. Not to be used in collector or in rock bin.

Closed-Cell Neoprene Gasket

Williams Products Inc., 1750 Maple Lawn Boulevard, Troy, MI 48084.

AIR HANDLING

Light-Duty Line Voltage Thermostats

Honeywell Stock No. 2E516, Dayton Stock No. 2E347, Grainger's, 5959 West Howard St., Chicago, IL 60648.

Relay

Magnecraft, 5575 N. Lynch Avenue, Chicago, IL 60630.

Two-Stage Thermostat with Subbase

Honeywell, General Offices, Minneapolis, MN 55408.

Low Leakage Dampers

Honeywell, General Offices, Minneapolis, MN 55408.
Arrow Pin-Lock, Arrow Louver & Damper Corp., 707 Concourse Village W., Bronx, NY 10451.

Back Draft Dampers

Arrow Pin-Lock, Arrow Louver & Damper Corp., 707 Concourse Village W., Bronx, NY 10451.
Contemporary Systems, Inc., Walpole, NH 03608.

Low-Voltage Motors for Dampers

Honeywell, General Offices, Minneapolis, MN 55408.

Differential Controller with Sensors

Honeywell, General Offices, Minneapolis, MN 55408.
Independent Energy C-30, P.O. Box 860, 42 Ladd St., East
   Greenwich, RI 02818.

Sensors

Dayton Remote Bulb SPDT Thermostat, (Stock No. 2E399),
   Grainger's, 5959 West Howard St., Chicago, IL 60648.
T67JA Series, Honeywell General Offices, Minneapolis, MN
   55408.

Blowers

Bayley, Propellair Group of Lau Division, Phillips Industries Inc.,
   843 Indianapolis Avenue, Lebanon, IN 46052.
Lau, 4540 West 160th Street, Cleveland, OH 44135.

Flexible Connectors, Ducts, and Duct Insulation

Williamson Co., 3500 Madison Road, Cincinnati, OH 45209.

Air Conditioning, Ventilating and Refrigeration Products

Grainger's, 5959 West Howard St., Chicago, IL 60648.

DHW PREHEAT SYSTEM

Anti-Syphon Device

Blazing Showers, P.O. Box 327, Point Arena, CA 95468.

Solar Tank

A. O. Smith, STJ30 through STJ120 (no internal hx), P.O. Box 28, Kankakee, IL 60901.

Pump (10 gpm)

Grundfos, 2555 Clovis Avenue, Clovis, CA 93612.

In-Duct Hot Water Coil

Trane Series 15-2 row, La Crosse, WI 54601.

Differential Controller with Sensors

Honeywell General Offices, Minneapolis, MN 55408.

Commercially Manufactured Air Handler

Rotaflow, Delta H Systems, Route 3, Sterling, CO 80751.
No Frills 1200, Contemporary Systems, Inc., Walpole, NH 03608.
Hot Stuff, 406 Walnut, La Jara, CO 81140.
Rocky Mountain Products, 5010 Cook Street, Denver, CO 80216.
Solar Control Corp., 5721 Arapahoe Rd., Boulder, CO 80302.
Solaron Corp., Solar Energy Systems, 300 Galleria Tower, 720 S. Colorado Blvd., Denver, CO 80222.
Heliotrope General, Inc., 3733 Kenora Drive, Spring Valley, CA 92077.
Park Energy Co., Star Route, Box 9, Jackson, WY 83001.
Helio Thermics, Inc., 1070 Orion St., Donaldson Ind. Park, Greenville, SC 29605.
Solar Development, Inc., 3323 Moline St., Aurora, CO 80010.
Tritec Solar Industries, Inc., 711 Florida Rd., P.O. Box 3145, Durango, CO 81301.

High-Temperature Duct Tape

3M Aluminum Foil Tape #425 will withstand continuous exposure to 300°F.
Available from:
1. Industrial distributors
2. Local automotive or hardware supply stores, as "Metal Repair Tape"

Overheating Alarm

Ademco Control Panel AD-1028 and Maintained Contact Switch #2174-70, Ademco, 165 Eileen Way, Soyosset, NY 11791.

APPENDIX B

DEVELOPMENTAL AND TECHNICAL DATA

B.1 CONCEPT

The purpose in developing this solar design was to significantly lower the cost of active solar systems by: (1) designing a collector which shares several of its components with the building, reducing duplication of materials; and (2) developing a low-cost delivery and storage system. Since commercially available active systems have only been marginally cost-effective in residential applications, T.E.A. believed the introduction of an effective low-cost design would fulfill a tremendous need. In the predicted growth of residential solar applications, there was clearly a definite role for economical active systems, even though passive solar systems prove an attractive option for much new construction. It was felt that for many buildings a combination of active and passive solar systems would be the best solution, while for others only one type would be appropriate.

Any new building design should be influenced by the principles of passive solar, at least to the extent of having some direct-gain windows on the south wall. In cases where it might be difficult to integrate a passive system requiring a large aperture area on the wall (for example, when a traditional house design is desired), the best option may be an active roof collector. In addition, in many climates the only way of achieving a high solar fraction (fraction of total heating need supplied by solar) is by combining both passive wall systems and active roof systems. Active collectors also have the advantage of permitting a large aperture area over a fully insulated wall or roof. This means the rate of heat loss or gain of the building is not increased—a particularly important consideration in cold climates which do not have a great deal of sun, and in climates which experience hot summers.

In retrofitting existing buildings for solar, active becomes a more promising option. Existing buildings often do not have a large wall area with a solar exposure, but do have a well-exposed roof. In this case, a large roof collector and a complete storage system is the best way to achieve a sizeable solar heating fraction. Even if there is a wall with good solar exposure, the plan of the house may not allow for the use of passive systems: for example, the south wall may be the garage wall. In these situations an active wall collector can be very useful,

FIG. B.1 DIRECT GAIN AND PASSIVE SYSTEMS AUGMENT EACH OTHER delivering the heat wherever it is most needed. If the collector area is not large, no storage is required (the collector being run only when heat is needed) and costs are dramatically reduced.

T.E.A. decided to develop an air system, rather than a liquid design, based on the consideration of a number of issues. Air collectors are simpler to build on-site for those without plumbing skills, and the collector materials are usually less expensive. The collectors are not subject to catastrophic freezing, and long-term corrosion is not a problem. The only long-term degradation problem is air leakage. The MODEL-TEA collector is initially assured to be airtight by incorporating a smoke test into the construction process; at anytime thereafter the collector can be retested and recaulked if leaks are suspected. Liquid collectors have the distinct advantage of a potentially higher heat removal efficiency factor (F_R). In addition, the liquid delivery and storage systems occupy much less space than those for air. Altogether the advantages and disadvantages of the two types of systems seem fairly equal. Our decision to develop an air system was influenced by the belief that it could produce a design which costs less, did not leak, and could be easily integrated (including ductwork) into most buildings.

The final design had to fulfill many criteria. In order to promote widespread use, it had to be low cost, simple, and easy to build using conventional techniques. Visual appearance was very important; the collector had to be considered an attractive addition to homes, or at least not an undesirable one. But, at the same time, the system had to perform well, be reliable, and maintain long-term durability under very demanding conditions of extreme temperature variations and weathering. This set of requirements established a very challenging project goal.

B.2 PROJECT DEVELOPMENT

T.E.A. began the project by conducting a nationwide survey of site-built installations. A detailed questionnaire was mailed to all site-builders who could be first contacted by phone and introduced to the project, and twenty questionnaires were returned. Descriptive information on materials used, problems

DEVELOPMENTAL AND
TECHNICAL DATA

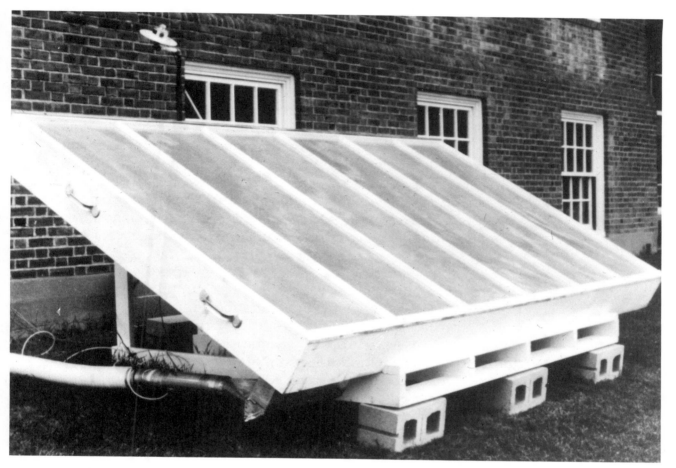

FIG. B.2 COLLECTOR TEST MODULE

experienced during construction, and durability of materials was fairly complete in most responses, while quantitative performance information was sketchy.

The next phase of the project was an extensive review of all materials available for site-fabricated air collectors. Information was gathered primarily from manufacturers, but data from many independent sources, such as testing laboratories and actual builders, were incorporated as well. Glazing materials, absorber plates, collector paints, sealants, fasteners, and structural materials were evaluated with respect to available sizes, physical properties, and cost. Particular emphasis was given to ease of handling, reliability, and durability.

The third phase of the project was the creation of six collector designs based on the questionnaire results, the materials survey, and T.E.A. design experience. Collector performance parameters were theoretically determined for each design, collector efficiency curves calculated, and annual performance determined in two cities using the f-Chart computer method. Material and labor costs were established for each design, and construction simplicity, building integration, reliability, durability, and aesthetics were evaluated. Through this process the T.E.A. staff selected the best design of the six. The project continued with the optimization of this design. The effects on collector performance of air mass flow rate, collector plate length, collector channel configuration, paint emissivity, insulation, and glazing alternatives were studied. In addition, procedures were developed to determine the optimum air flow rate, collector path length, and channel size for various specific applications.

To pursue the study of this optimum design, five collector test modules were constructed and tested according to strict industry test procedures (ASHRAE 93-77 standards and the HUD 30-day stagnation test). A standard, commercially manufactured air collector was tested on the same equipment for direct comparison. This allowed not only a direct check of the site-fabricated design vs. the manufactured, but also allowed a comparison with testing results on the manufactured collector obtained by another nationally recognized independent testing laboratory. The overall purpose of the testing program was to provide basic performance numbers for comparison with the theoretical predictions, and to allow a direct evaluation of the collector modules, including such considerations as durability, ease of construction, weathering, and aesthetics. The modules differed in the types of glazing material, absorber surface, and amount of caulking material.

The testing program produced a wealth of valuable information. The measured efficiency of the basic design showed excellent agreement with T.E.A.'s theoretical calculations. In addition, after more than 30 days of summertime stagnation, the collector efficiency did not decrease. The test modules showed no degradation due to weathering or high temperature stagnation. All the collector modules were tested for leakage, and the results demonstrated that eliminating leaks is probably the most

FIG. B.3 FAILURE OF ACRYLIC IN GLAZING TEST

critical aspect of site-building an air collector. As a result of
these tests, T.E.A. has specified a smoke test as an integral part
of the construction process, and it has been demonstrated in
actual installations that the collector can readily be made airtight.

One of the most valuable results of the testing program was
the conclusions on glazing materials. Although the project staff
preferred glass, due in large part to aesthetic considerations,
three types of plastic glazing materials were tested on the modules. One type was a total failure, and the other two showed
serious problems, making glass the ultimate choice (see Section

A.1). The search for a method of fastening the glass to the collector resulted in three alternatives and, to assist in choosing among these, another testing program was begun. A full scale mock-up of a 60°-tilt roof was constructed, and the three glazing systems were mounted side by side. The test provided information about the ease of installation and weathering characteristics of each system. With the final selection of a glazing system, the collector design was completed.

The next major phase of the project was the development of the air-handling systems. After surveying current designs, T.E.A. began work on a simple, low-cost design which could be integrated into existing buildings or used in new construction. For small collectors (usually on walls), only a very simple system was required, as no storage would be employed. In these applications, a fan and ductwork would deliver the heated air from the collector directly to the living space whenever there was both demand for heat and sufficient sunshine. But for larger collectors, a storage rock bin would be used, and a more complicated air-handling system would be required. It was important that this system not depend on any particular building configuration, since it had to be adaptable to either new construction or retrofit.

There were basically two approaches, employing either a commercially manufactured air handler, or one built on-site from separate components. Most manufactured residential air handlers cost more than $2000, including controls, although there are two innovative products available for approximately $1300. Separate components can be purchased to build a system on site for roughly $1300. The labor cost of the site-built air handler increases the total cost to roughly the same as that of the standard commercial air handlers, but the site-built product is of better quality. By buying separate components and assembling on site, the fans and dampers can be better integrated into the ductwork. This results in two major advantages. First, during construction it is easier to accommodate the relative positions of the rock bin and duct runs. It can be difficult to install a manufactured air handler in a limited space, especially in retrofit situations where positions of rock bins and duct runs are dictated by other considerations. Secondly, since the site-assembled system allows for straighter duct runs and less bends near fans, the pressure drops are lower, resulting in greater system efficiency.

Thus the site-assembled air handler was preferred over the manufactured version, despite similar costs. The $1300 innovative commercial air handlers (see Chapter 8) were, however, attractive alternatives. Still, the project staff preferred not to depend solely on one or two commercial products, especially innovative designs which had not experienced widespread use. This consideration was the basis for one of the major advantages of the site-assembled system; all of the components could be purchased from more than one source, and had proven track records. However, the commercial air handlers discussed in Section 8.1 may prove to be the best answer for many applications. They offer a significant advantage in simplifying the installation of both air-handling equipment and controls.

Based on T.E.A.'s research, and its experience with design and installation of solar air-heating systems, a final design was completed which uses two fans and three standard, low-leakage dampers. In existing buildings this system is installed independently of the present conventional heating system (in parallel). This enables a straightforward installation, no matter what type of heating system is present. In new construction, the solar system replaces a conventional heating system. Auxiliary heating is accomplished by inserting the heater in the ductwork so it is in series with the solar system, resulting in beneficial preheating by solar even when the latter cannot carry the entire load. This series installation is possible in new construction since the auxiliary can be carefully integated with the design of the solar system, and since new buildings do not require an extensive heat distribution system, due to their high level of insulation. Thus, a properly designed new building (Chapter 2) can result in a substantial savings due to the synthesis of the solar and auxiliary heating systems.

In addition to this relatively conventional air-handling system, T.E.A. developed an innovative system suitable only for new construction. This design allows a substantial cost savings for buildings where the designer is willing to carefully integrate the system needs with the building design. The system utilizes a one-way rock bed, one fan, and two mechanically connected dampers. The rock bed is integrated into a wall or under a floor. This design is described in detail in Chapter 8.

The rock bin which accompanies the conventional air system in either new or existing buildings is a proven T.E.A. design. It is a two-way rock bin which uses a compact U-shaped air-flow path, allowing for duct connections at the top, low height, and simple construction.

The only remaining project task was the design of controls to govern the air-handling systems. Consistent with the overall philosophy of the project, a site-assembled control system was developed. The controls utilize standard components which can be purchased from a number of sources. The completion of the control system constituted the final phase of the design development.

B.3 MAJOR DESIGN DECISIONS

Two categories of key design decisions are discussed here, the first relating to problems caused by high temperatures in the collector, and the second dealing with air-handling and storage matters. The collector normally operates at about 140°F, and all the collector materials can easily tolerate these temperatures indefinitely. However, if the roof collector is allowed to stagnate in the summer (no air flow), temperatures up to 250°F or even 300°F will be reached. This only occurs with the roof collector, not the wall collector. The vertical wall collector does not receive enough solar radiation from the high summer sun to reach temperatures above 250°F. The tilted roof collector receives much more radiation from the high sun angle, especially if, instead of being at the optimum tilt (latitude plus 15°), it is at a lower pitch (say 30°) in a retrofit application. During the summer season, a stagnating 30°-tilt roof collector would experience temperatures above 250°F for roughly 600 hours in Massachusetts, and 1000 hours in New Mexico. Maximum temperatures would be near 350°F.

While these high temperatures do not cause immediate failure of any part of the collector, the long-term effect of temperatures above 250°F is to accelerate the aging process. The EPDM, caulk, and any wood in or near the collector, are particularly susceptible to accelerated degradation above 250°F. Expansion and contraction of the absorber plate also become more severe at these temperatures. All these factors combine to shorten the lifetime of the collector and increase the probability of developing air leaks. Even the wood in the rafters under the Thermo-ply would begin to suffer significant drying and weight loss over a long period of time.

There are basically two ways to deal with these temperature problems. One is to simply let the collector stagnate every summer, but choose materials and a design such that no serious degradation will result for at least twenty years. The other approach is to prevent the collector temperature from rising above 250°F by either venting the collector or shading it from the sun. T.E.A. explored both alternatives. The first approach, designing for stagnation, was studied and rejected. Wood could easily be removed from the collector by replacing the wooden inner battens with aluminum (see Chapter 8). In addition the rafters could be protected from high temperatures by replacing the Thermo-ply with a better insulator, such as a high temperature insulation. But the major problems with the caulking, EPDM, and the thermal stresses on the absorber remain. While short-term exposures to high temperatures are not a problem, the long-term effects of many thousands of hours above 250°F cause significant degradation.

The second approach, preventing temperature rise above 250°F, was adopted. Consideration was given to shading the roof collector, perhaps with a roll-down cover or some other seasonally positioned shade. But the use of any such cover is accompanied by a number of problems. The cover must be very strong and durable to withstand high winds and long-term weathering. Visual appearance is important; it should either be very attractive or blend in with the roof. A requirement of manual seasonal placement presents a serious disadvantage, since many users might procrastinate, or perhaps fail to use the cover. And one of the most serious problems is that with the summertime cover in place, the collector cannot be used to heat domestic hot water. Probably the option which comes closest to satisfying all requirements is a partial shading accomplished by either a whitewash on the glass, or bamboo curtain or snow fence fastened securely to the collector. An appropriate amount of partial shading together with running the fan for domestic hot water will protect the collector from excessive temperatures. However, these options still do not meet the objections of visual appearance and user participation.

The other means of preventing excessive temperature rise is venting the collector. Venting can be accomplished either by thermosiphoning (natural vertical flow of heated air) or by using the fan to power vent. In order to maintain the collector temperature within reasonable limits, a minimum air flow of 2 CFM per square foot of collector must be assured. This flow rate is difficult to achieve by thermosiphoning without a very large cross-sectional area of vent openings. In many collector designs, it is nearly impossible to successfully integrate a sufficiently large vent area. In addition, a large vent area is very difficult to seal. At the beginning of each heating season the user must insure that all vents are closed, absolutely airtight. Another problem with natural venting is associated with the fact that the space most readily vented is that between the glazing and the absorber. Venting this area allows air to flow under the glazing, resulting in an accumulation of dirt. This reduces transmittance and is impossible to clean without totally removing the glazing. A final problem is cost—the cost of installing such a large vent area is almost as great as the cost of power venting.

T.E.A. decided to protect the collector by power venting. This option does not require any alterations whatsoever to the collector, and affects only the air-handling system. Two extra duct runs to the outside are required, along with two manual guillotine-type dampers. It is critical that these dampers are perfectly sealed at the beginning of the heating season, but that is easily done since they are so small and accessible. The power venting mode, engaged seasonally, takes in outside air, blows it through the collector at the standard flow rate, and returns it to the outside. The electrical operating cost of the fan is approximately $25 to $35 per year for an operating time of 1000 to 1400 hours, the time necessary to keep the collector temperature below 200°F.

Most roof system installations will use domestic hot water (DHW) coils in the system ductwork. The collector will be cooled somewhat by the fan running in the summer to provide DHW, and T.E.A. originally thought that this DHW-related fan operation might be sufficient to entirely cool the collector. However, computer simulations were conducted and they showed that additional power venting was necessary. Thus, the only way the collector temperature could rise above 200°F is if the power venting system failed. T.E.A. decided to include a high-temperature alarm to warn the homeowner any time the collector temperature exceeded the acceptable range.

The second category of major decisions deals with the air-handling and storage systems. As discussed in Section B.2, Project Development, essentially three system options were developed: (1) a simple one-fan, no-storage system for small collectors; (2) a site-assembled conventional type system utilizing a two-way rock bin, suitable for either retrofit or new construction; and (3) a low-cost innovative system employing a one-way rock bed, requiring careful engineering, and only suitable for new construction. A number of important design decisions were involved in the development of the conventional two-way rock bin system. This basic system was chosen because it is proven, flexible, and reliable, but careful planning was required to make the system efficient for both new and retrofit situations.

A fundamental decision was made to install the solar sytem in parallel with the auxiliary for retrofit, and in series for new construction. In some cases, existing buildings being retrofitted with air site-built systems may already have forced-hot-air heating systems. However, the solar system often cannot be simply connected to the existing ductwork. The solar air-handling system must be properly balanced, and often the pressure drop in the existing delivery ductwork may be larger than optimum. Active solar air systems are significantly different than standard forced-air systems. Air is moved in larger volumes, and pressure drops and leakage are more critical. Undersizing of ducts or blowers reduces the volumetric air flow rate which tends to lower the collector efficiency and reduce performance. The house distribution system must be carefully sized to avoid these difficulties. So even though the existing auxiliary is forced air,

FIG. B.4 SOLAR COLLECTOR UNDER CONSTRUCTION

new ductwork may be required to move the solar system air to
the living space.

In many retrofit installations, the building will have a different
type of heating system, such as hot water or steam, and thus the
solar system must be considered to be a separate heating system. T.E.A. decided that the best solution to all these retrofit
situations was to have one design which was always installed

separately from the existing auxiliary. The control system en-
sures that the two systems are efficiently used, although they do
not share the same delivery system.

In retrofitting the MODEL-TEA to multistory buildings with
basements or crawl spaces, the solar heated air should be supplied only to the first floor. This eliminates the difficult problem
of integrating new ductwork into the living space. If the house
has been properly insulated prior to the solar installation, there
should be good mixing of heated air. In some cases, particularly where the collector is capable of meeting the entire house
heating load over a good part of the year, it may be advisable to
install through-the-floor grills between the first and second floor
to improve air circulation. The floor and ceiling grills can be
horizontally offset to afford visual privacy. In cases where the
collector area is small and the house heating load large, a
zoned auxiliary by floors can be considered. Thus, in houses
with basements, it is reasonable to locate the rock bin, air-
handling equipment, and all the delivery ductwork there.

Retrofitting houses on slabs presents a more difficult building
integration problem. The rock bin and air-handling equipment
must be integrated into a space on the first floor, and the
ductwork must be fitted into the ceiling. The only alternative is
to use a smaller collector area and an air system without storage. This will be the most attractive option for many applications because of its low initial cost.

Since in retrofit applications the solar system is in parallel with
the auxiliary, the control system must be carefully designed to
allow optimum utilization of the solar heat. A system which
stopped solar heated air flow to the living space whenever the
entire heating load could not be met would definitely not be
desirable. If this were the case, much useful solar heat would
be wasted. T.E.A.'s control design for retrofit systems delivers
solar-heated air to the living space whenever both the house
thermostat calls for heat and the solar-heated air is above 85°F.
If more heat is required, it is provided by the auxiliary heating
system simultaneously.

In new construction this situation does not exist, since the solar
and auxiliary systems are in series. The auxiliary heater is
placed in the solar-to-house ductwork, so that solar-heated air
always passes through the auxiliary on its way to the living

space. If the solar air temperature is not sufficient to meet the house load, the second stage of the thermostat activates the auxiliary. Thus air heated by the auxiliary has been preheated by either the collector or rock bin, assuring good utilization of solar energy.

Some of the problems associated with retrofit can be designed away in new construction. A basement or utility room area can be planned for the rock bin, well-integrated duct runs from the collector to the basement can be provided, and there is more flexibility in the design of the duct system to the living space. A new building can be better insulated than a retrofit case, and with full insulation a more even temperature distribution will exist in the living space. Thus heated air need only be supplied to the first floor, and if necessary, through-the-floor grills can be used to circulate air to a floor above. If desired, the return air system can be used to circulate second-floor air back down to the first floor. Finally, with well-insulated new construction the building heating load is smaller, so the entire solar system and auxiliary can be made smaller and more efficient.

As another option for new construction, T.E.A. decided to develop a low-cost innovative system, applicable to buildings which could be carefully designed to accommodate the solar system. This system employs a one-way rock bed in close proximity to both the collector and living space. Although this design requires more careful sizing and engineering than the conventional system, it can perform as well and at a much lower cost. The innovative system is explained in Section 8.2.

B.4 TECHNICAL INFORMATION

Collector Efficiency

The information in Figure B.5 is for a 16 × 20 ft MODEL-TEA collector with a volumetric air flow rate of 3 CFM per square foot.

	F_R	U_L (Btu/hr ft² F)	$(\tau\alpha)$
SINGLE GLASS	0.72	1.10	0.86
DOUBLE GLASS	0.80	0.65	0.78

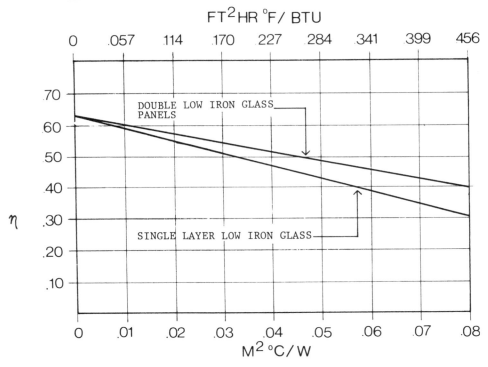

FIG. B.5 EFFICIENCY OF FULL-SIZE COLLECTOR

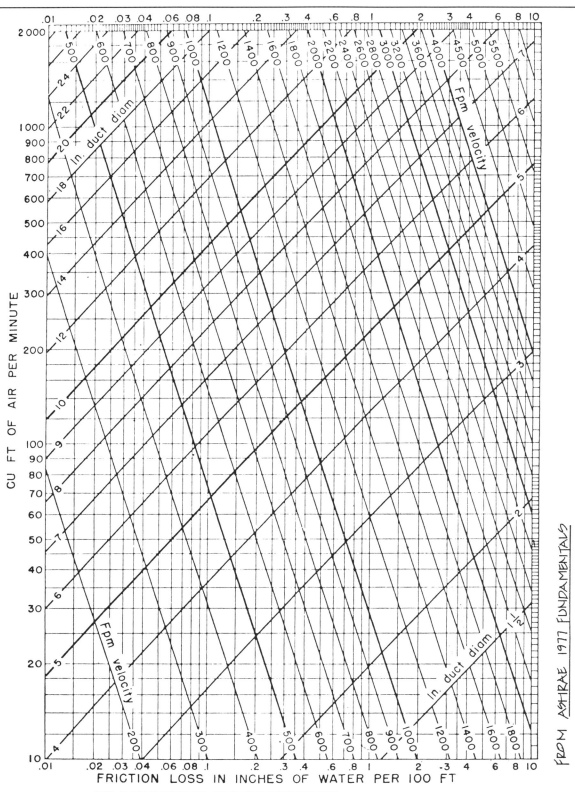

FIG. B.6 FRICTION OF AIR IN STRAIGHT DUCTS
FOR VOLUMES OF 10 TO 2000 CFM. REPRINTED BY PERMISSION FROM
1977 ASHRAE HANDBOOK OF FUNDAMENTALS.

System Information

The following system technical parameters were used in the
f-Chart computer performance calculations.

Storage capacity	15 Btu/°F ft²
Effective building UA	625 Btu/hr°F
Constant daily building heat generation	2500 Btu/hr
Hot water usage	60 gal/day
Water set temperature	140°F
Water main temperature	55°F

Related Technical Papers

"Evaluation of Six Designs for a Site-Fabricated, Building Integrated Air Heater. Part I: Theoretical Performance," *Proceedings of the 1978 Annual Meeting of the American Section of the International Solar Energy Society*, Vol. 2.1. (September, 1978), J. Coleman, J. Kohler, P. Sullivan, P. Temple.

"Evaluation of Six Designs for a Site-Fabricated, Building Integrated Air Heater, Part II: Cost, Seasonal Performance, Building Integration, Reliability and Aesthetics," *Proceedings of the 1978 Annual Meeting of the American Section of the International Solar Energy Society*, Vol. 2.1 (September, 1978), J. Coleman, J. Kohler, P. Sullivan, P. Temple.

"Development of a Site-Fabricated, Building Integrated Air Collector, Part I: Evaluation of Alternative Collector Designs," *Proceedings of the First Annual New England Site-Built Collector Conference*, (December, 1978), J. Coleman, J. Kohler, P. Sullivan, P. Temple.

"The MODEL-TEA Site-Fabricated Building Integrated Air Collector, (June 1979), ASHRAE Annual Meeting, J. Kohler, P. Sullivan, P. Temple.

"A Proven, Cost-Effective, Building Integrated Site-Built Solar Heating System," *Proceedings of the Fifth National Passive Solar Conference*, American Section of the ISES, University of Delaware, Newark, DE, P. Temple, J. Kohler.

RECOMMENDED READING

BOOKS

The Solar Home Book: Heating, Cooling and Designing with the Sun, Bruce Anderson; Brick House Publishing Co., Andover, MA (1976)

Passive Solar Energy, Bruce Anderson and Malcolm Wells; Brick House Publishing, Co., Andover, MA (1981)

Solar Heating Design by the f-Chart Method, William A. Beckman, Sanford A. Klein, John A. Duffie; John Wiley & Sons, New York, NY (1977)

Fundamentals, ASHRAE Handbook & Product Directory, 1977; ASHRAE, New York, NY (1977)

Installation Standard for One & Two Family Dwellings and Multi-family Housing including Solar, Sheet Metal and Air Conditioning Contractors National Association, Inc., 8224 Old Courthouse Road, Tyson's Corner, Vienna, VA (1977)

"Model Document for Code Officials on Solar Heating & Cooling of Buildings," Second Draft, U.S. Department of Energy, Washington, D.C. (1979). (Not a law; does show how to use solar to comply with local building codes.)

MAGAZINES

Solar Age. SolarVision, Harrisville, NH 03450. (Monthly. $20 per year. Articles on projects, ideas, events, new procedures.)

Solar Engineering Magazine, 8435 N. Stemmons Freeway, Dallas, TX 75247. (Monthly. $15 per year. Information about products and systems.)

New Shelter. Rodale, 33 East Minor St., Emmaus, PA 18049. (9 times a year. $9 per year. Emphasis on do-it-yourself projects.)

ORGANIZATIONS AND INFORMATION SOURCES

National Solar Heating and Cooling Information Center, Franklin Research Center, Philadelphia, PA 19103. Hotline. (800) 523-2929 or in Pennsylvania (800) 462-4983. In Alaska and Hawaii call (800) 523-4700. *Information on all aspects of solar energy.*

State Energy Offices. Call the National Solar Heating and Cooling Information Center (see above) for latest listing for your state.

Federal and State Incentives. Call the National Solar Heating and Cooling Information Center for latest Federal incentives and your State Energy Office for those applying to your state.

Brace Research Institute, McGill University, Montreal, P.Q. Canada. *Plans, books and reports.*

Farallones Institute, 1516 Fifth St., Berkeley, CA 94710. *Plans, books and reports.*

National Center for Appropriate Technology, 3040 Continental Drive, Butte, MT 59701. *Fact sheets, pamphlets.*

National Climatic Center, Federal Building, Asheville, NC. *Weather data.*

New Alchemy Institute, P.O. Box 432, Woods Hole, MA 02543. *Books, journal and reports.*

INDEX

Page numbers in **bold** indicate information found in illustrations.

MODEL-TEA SOLAR HEATING SYSTEM OWNER'S MANUAL

NOTICE: If you build and install your own MODEL-TEA Solar Heating System, this manual will be a valuable reminder for regular service and maintenance procedures. If you, the owner of this book, are a contractor, please keep the manual in the book for reference. Write to T.E.A. to obtain additional copies for the homeowners whose systems you install: it is critical that you supply this information to the homeowner to ensure that maintenance procedures are performed as required, and that the alarm system and other signs of malfunction are readily understood.

Additional copies are available from:

Owner's Manual
Total Environmental Action, Inc.
Church Hill
Harrisville, NH 03450

(603) 827-3361

Your MODEL-TEA Solar Heating System should provide many years of efficient and reliable service, and result in significant savings in the cost of heating your home. To use your solar heating system most efficiently, you should be familiar with its normal operation and the routine maintenance that is required.

Most homeowners have their local heating company perform an annual inspection and maintenance check on their conventional heating system (oil or gas furnace). Your solar heating system should also receive periodic inspections by a knowledgeable person. If you did not build your system yourself, and do not understand it completely, you probably should have a trained professional provide regular inspections. The company that installed your system may be your best choice to provide that service. The company you hire to do routine inspections should also be available for repair work if a problem occurs with your solar system.

Remember that your installer is your best source of information on maintenance and operation. The installer knows the particular type of system you have and can give you specific instructions on its proper care. This owner's manual is only meant to be a general guide that applies to most typical systems.

Normal System Operation

You should be familiar with the normal operation of your solar heating sytem, so that you will recognize any signs that the system is not operating as it should. There are a number of variations of the MODEL-TEA system, and your installer should explain to you the essentials of your particular version. The following basics apply to most systems.

On cold, sunny days when your house needs heat, the system should be running and delivering warm air through the registers. Your furnace (conventional backup heating system) should not have to run much, if at all, on such days.

On cold, cloudy days when your house needs heat, the solar system will not run (since there is no sunshine). If your system

3

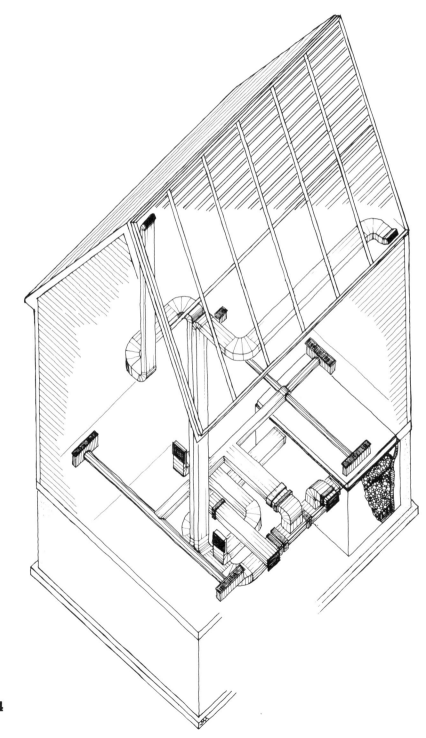

includes a rock storage bin, that rock bin may contain surplus heat that was collected on the previous sunny day. The system will deliver to the house any useful heat which remains in the rock bin. However, this heat will often be consumed during the night following the day on which it was collected (depending upon the particular house and system design). Thus, on most cloudy days you will rely on your backup system.

In spring and summer weather, your house should not require any heat, either from the solar system or the backup system. Your solar system may still operate, but not in a house-heating mode. It may operate either to power-vent the collector or to heat domestic hot water (DHW). If you have a roof collector (sloped, not vertical), your collector must be power-vented in the summer. In the spring, at the end of the heating season, you must change the system to the power-vent mode. Then, in the summer, whenever the collector temperature reaches 180°F, power-venting will automatically start. Outside air will be drawn through the collector, heated (thereby cooling the collector), and exhausted back to the outside. Thus power-venting will not affect the cooling or air conditioning of the interior of the house in any way. When the collector has been sufficiently cooled, the power-venting will automatically stop. You should notice that the power-venting is running during the hottest hours of sunny days, and it should not run at all on very cloudy days.

Your MODEL-TEA solar system may also include provisions for heating domestic hot water (DHW). If it does, the system should run on most sunny summer days. The more hot water you use, the more the system will run. If you use a great deal of hot water in the morning, you will notice that the system runs more during the day to reheat your water tank. Of course, on dark, overcast days the system will not run.

If you have a vertical wall collector which does not require power-venting, and you do not use your system to heat hot water, your system should not operate at all during the summer.

As you become accustomed to the system's operation, you will learn to recognize the sound of the fan running and the feel of

5

warm air coming from the registers. You should also recognize the sound your furnace makes. If you ever notice any signs that something is operating improperly, you should call your repair service company.

Operation and Maintenance Procedures

The daily operation of the MODEL-TEA system is automatic, controlled by "thermostats" much the way a conventional heating system is controlled. However, twice each year a manual operation is required. In the spring, at the end of the heating season, the space-heating mode of the system should be halted. That is done by shutting off the differential controller. Once that is done, the system will no longer try to heat either the house or the rock storage bin. In the fall, when the heating season begins again, the differential controller must be turned on. Then the system will again be able to heat the house.

If you have a *roof* collector (as opposed to a vertical wall collector), your system is equipped with a power-venting mode. The power-venting mode must be engaged in the summertime. The exact procedure for switching from the heating to the power-venting mode should be demonstrated to you by your installer. The general procedure will involve: (1) shutting off the differential controller; (2) moving the two manual slide dampers from winter to summer position; and (3) changing the power-vent switch from winter to summer position. The first step, shutting off (or disconnecting) the differential controller, disengages the heating mode. This should be done no matter what type of system you have. The second step, moving the manual slide dampers, is essential for proper operation of the power-venting and/or summertime DHW modes. This summertime damper position allows outside air to be brought in, pulled through the collector, and exhausted back to the outside. The third step, changing the power-vent switch from winter to summer position, engages the power-venting mode, so that whenever the collector temperature rises above 180°F, the collector will automatically be power-vented.

If the power-venting system were not engaged, or were to malfunction, the roof collector could overheat on sunny days, reaching temperatures as high as 300 to 350°F. If the collector were allowed to experience excessively high temperatures for long periods of time, serious degradation of the materials would occur. This could not only cause the collector to perform poorly (develop air leaks), but could even result in a fire.

In the heating season, normal collector operating temperatures do not exceed 140°F. In the summer, the power-venting system will prevent the temperature of your roof collector from exceeding 180°F. If the power-venting system fails to operate on a sunny summer day, the collector temperature will continue to rise and at 200°F an alarm will be triggered. This overheating alarm should alert you to the problem so that immediate steps can be taken to correct whatever malfunction caused the overheating. Short exposure (a few days) to these excessive temperatures will not cause serious damage, but exposure for a few weeks or longer could have serious consequences. If the alarm is disabled, and the malfunction is not corrected, not only could the collector suffer serious permanent damage, but a building fire could be ignited. Thus, if your overheating alarm ever sounds, you should notify your repair service immediately.

If your MODEL-TEA system has a *vertical* wall collector (rather than a sloped roof collector), you will not have a power-venting system, and overheating will not be a problem. Since the summer sun is at such a high angle in the sky, much less sunlight will strike the wall collector than would strike a roof collector. Thus, excessively high temperatures will not be reached.

There are a few other items of routine maintenance. You may wish to have these done by your professional service company, or you may wish to do some of these yourself. In order to receive optimum performance from your collector, the glass should be kept clean to allow the maximum amount of light to be transmitted to the absorber. Cleaning the glass once per year should be sufficient. The motors and dampers in the air-handling system should be oiled and checked annually.

Summary of Operation and Maintenance Procedures

1. No matter what type of system you have, you should shut off the differential controller at the end of the heating season, and turn it back on in the fall.

2. If you have a roof-mounted collector (which must be power-vented), you also must change the two manual dampers from winter to summer positions and you must change the power-vent switch from winter to summer. In the fall, you must reverse the process.

3. If you have a roof-mounted collector, you will have an over-*heating alarm*. If this alarm sounds, call your repair service company immediately and arrange for the situation to be corrected. If overheating persists, a dangerous situation, even a fire, could result.

4. Other routine maintenance can be accomplished on an annual basis. You may wish to have this done along with an annual inspection, by a professional service company familiar with your system.